AIRCRAFT CONSTRUCTION HANDBOOK

ISBN: 1940001323

The Aviation Collection
by
Sportsman's Vintage Press
2015

Aircraft Construction Handbook

By Thomas A. Dickinson

U. S. Navy Aircraft Inspector at
Consolidated Aircraft Corporation

Originally published in 1943

TO MY WIFE STEPHANIE

PREFACE

This book is an introduction to the business of building airplanes; it should be valuable either as part of a course for beginners or as a reference for persons with some practical experience.

Since there is but little in modern science that should not be of interest to an ambitious aircraft worker, it is virtually impossible to present in a single volume all the information that *might be* of value. However, an effort has been made to touch on the more pertinent subjects and to provide a background which will make advanced studies practicable. For example, Chapter 2 contains all the information the average aircraft worker should require on the subject of aerodynamics; yet the sum total of human knowledge in this field could easily fill a small library.

Photographs and drawings are used in this book as an integral part of the text. It is the author's belief that a single good illustration will tell more than thousands of even the most carefully chosen words. Therefore, it has been found possible to present in a comparatively small amount of space more than a primary quota of technical information.

Whenever possible, simplified explanations of all "technical" terms have been made in the text. However, since the author has no means of determining the reader's background and experience, an extensive Glossary of technical terms was also found necessary. It is recommended that the reader refer to this list whenever he encounters a word or phrase he does not immediately comprehend.

The Appendix should be a worth-while reference in any branch of the aircraft industry.

THOMAS A. DICKINSON

ACKNOWLEDGMENTS

For their help in contributing illustrations and technical information for this volume, the author expresses thanks to the following persons and concerns:

Douglas B. Hobbs, Aluminum Company of America
American Society for Metals
W. H. McDaniel, Beech Aircraft Corporation
Bethlehem Steel Company
Harold Mansfield, Boeing Aircraft Company
Bureau of Aeronautics, U.S. Navy
Douglas T. Kelley, Consolidated Aircraft Corporation
F. O. Schubert, Consolidated Aircraft Corporation
A. M. Rochlen, Douglas Aircraft Company, Inc.
John W. Thompson, Ford Motor Company
L. R. Grumman, Grumman Aircraft Engineering Corporation
George I. Willis, Hamilton Standard Propellers
Maxwell Stiles, Lockheed Aircraft Corporation
National Advisory Committee for Aeronautics
Carl Apponyi, Northrop Aircraft, Inc.
Tom Hall Miller, Piper Aircraft Corporation
William Wagner, Ryan Aeronautical Company
San Diego Vocational High School and Junior College
T. A. Bissell, The Society of Automotive Engineers
Robert S. Burnett, The Society of Automotive Engineers
H. E. Masters, The L. S. Starrett Company
U.S. Army Air Forces
Frank J. Delear, Vought-Sikorsky Aircraft

I am especially grateful to the public relations department of the Consolidated Aircraft Corporation for their untiring assistance in obtaining photographs and drawings. And, for their more immediate technical efforts and advice, I am indebted to Messrs. W. T. Dugas, E. H. Lang, and H. R. Weeks of the U. S. Navy Inspection service; Mr. Donald Lilly of the San Diego Vocational High School and Junior College; Mr. F. W. Zellmer of the Consolidated Aircraft Corporation; and Mr. Robert L. Crowell of the Thomas Y. Crowell Company.

Tables, illustrations, and other data accredited to the Aluminum Company of America are from the following copyrighted booklets: *Welding Aluminum, Aluminum in Aircraft, ALCOA Aluminum and Its Alloys, Machining Alcoa Aluminum.*

The material accredited to The Society of Automotive Engineers is reprinted from the 1942 edition of the S.A.E. Handbook, by permission of that organization.

T. A. D.

CONTENTS

CHAPTER   PAGE

1. How an Airplane Factory Operates   1

Administration   1
Customer Representatives   2
Experimental and Planning   2
Production Engineering   3
Project Coordinators   3
Plant Maintenance   3
Parts and Processes   4
Primary Assembly   5
Final Assembly   7
Inspection   7
Salvage   8
Flight Test and Service Departments   8

2. Aerodynamics   9

Air Forces 10
The Davis and Northrup Wings 12

3. Aircraft Types and Nomenclature 13

General Construction Characteristics 14
Stationing 17
Power-Plant Nomenclature 17
Surface Controls 19
Wing Nomenclature 21
Fuselage Nomenclature 23
Tail Sections 23
Landing Gear Nomenclature 26
Seaplanes, Flying Boats, and Amphibians 27

xi

CHAPTER   PAGE
4. Aircraft Design Principles 28
    Choosing an Airfoil Section 29
    Wind-Tunnel Tests 30
    Mock-up 30
    Stress Analysis 31
    Detailed Design 32
    Lofting 33

5. Materials and Processes. 38
    Metallurgy 39
    Metallurgical Tests 41
    Heat Treatment 42
    Annealing 43
    Aluminum and Its Alloys 44
    Surface Protection for Aluminum Alloys 47
    Working with Aluminum and Its Alloys 48
    Airplane Steels 51
    Special Steel Processes 56
    Magnesium and Its Alloys 58
    Beryllium 60
    Alloying Elements 61
    Metalizing or Metal Spraying 64
    Cadmium Plating 64
    Plastics 67
    Dopes and Fabrics 70
    Neoprene and Thiokol 71

6. Shop Practice 73
    Drafting 74
    Drafting Rules 77
    Specifications 79
    Bolts and Screws 87
    Nuts and Washers 88
    Turnbuckle Assemblies 91
    Control Pulleys 92
    Cotter Pins 93

CHAPTER   PAGE
Taper Pins 94
Dzus Fasteners 94
Dill Lok-Skru Fastener 96
Explosive Rivets 98
Goodrich Riv-Nuts 99
Measuring Instruments 101
Bending Allowances 107
Aircraft Tubing and Fittings 113
Flaring 113
Torque Wrenches 116
Socket Wrenches 118
Screwdrivers 118
Taps and Dies 119
Files 120
Joggling 122

7. Assembly 123
Jigs and Fixtures 124
Riveting 126
Welding 134

8. Inspection 148
Types of Inspection 149

Appendix 157
1. Weights and Specific Gravities 157
2. Colors of Steel at Various Temperatures . . . 158
3. Conditions for Heat Treatment of Aluminum Alloys 158
4. Aging Details 159
5. Commercial Aluminum Alloys 160
6. Heat-Treatment Procedure for Structural Steels . 161
7. Strength and Specification Numbers for Aluminum
   Alloys 162
8. Strength and Specification Numbers for Steel . . 164
9. Standard Color Chart for Raw Materials . . . 166
10. Standard Sizes of Rivets with Chamfered Shank . 169

xiv *Contents*

CHAPTER   PAGE
11. Centigrade and Fahrenheit Temperature Equivalents 170
12. Bend Radii Information 171
13. Joggle Chart for Extruded Sections 172
14. Abbreviations Used on Aircraft Blueprints . . . 173
15. Aircraft Finish Code 175
16. Different Standards for Wire Gages in Use in the
    United States 177
17. Hardness Conversion Table 178
18. Screw Threads and Tap Drill Sizes 180
19. Drill Sizes 181
20. Chemical Elements and Symbols 182
21. Conversion Factors 184
22. Decimal Equivalents of Fractions of an Inch . . . 186
23. Rules Relative to the Circle, etc. 187
24. Functions of Numbers 188
25. Table for Solving Right-Angled Triangles . . . 192

Glossary 193

Bibliography 223

Index 229

THE AIRCRAFT WORKER'S
TEN COMMANDMENTS

1. Thou shalt make mistakes, but thou shalt not cover them up; for he who conceals a flaw in an airplane is a criminal indeed.
2. Consult thou an engineer when in doubt about the construction of any part.
3. Depend not on the inspector to discover thy mistakes, for he is only human.
4. Remember thou, the Union can get thee more pay; but only thou can be worth it.
5. Watch thy fingers, if thou wouldst keep same.
6. Wear goggles when around flying bits of metal, and observe all safety rules.
7. Follow thy specifications, for verily they tell what the customer wants.
8. Boast not of thy knowledge, lest thy boss take thee for a fool.
9. Study hard, and thou shalt be amply rewarded.
10. Know thy job thoroughly, for some day thou mayst fly in an airplane thy hand hast wrought.

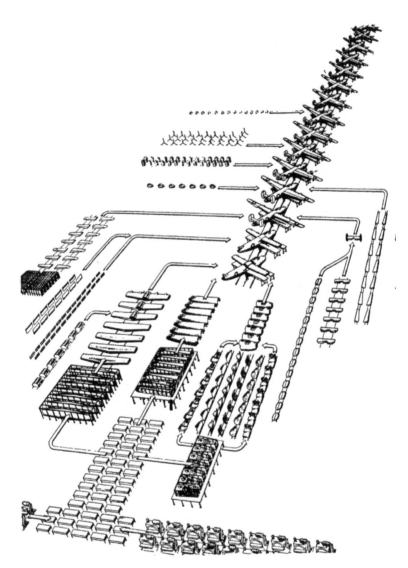

FLOW CHART FOR HEAVY BOMBERS—PARTS AND PROCESSES TO FINAL ASSEMBLY
(Consolidated Aircraft Corp.)

TYPICAL FACTORY ORGANIZATION CHART

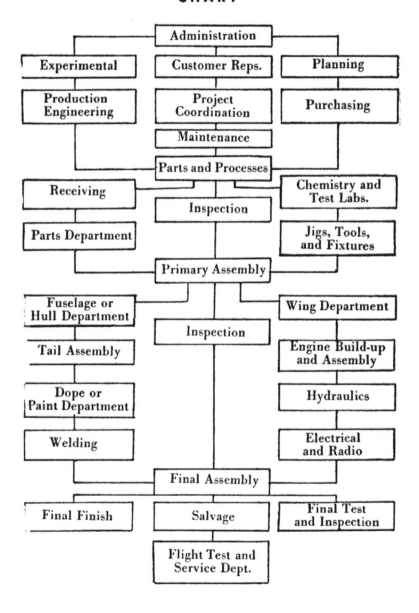

1

HOW AN AIRPLANE FACTORY
OPERATES

While no two American aircraft factories have precisely the same organizational setup, they are on the whole similar and can be compared structurally to an army brigade. Perhaps this is because military aviation has long been the most important customer to so many manufacturers.

The "general" of the airplane factory "brigade" is, of course, the president of the company; his "staff" is the administration department; and his "troops" are the remainder of the plant.

"Special troops" are the designers, engineers, maintenance men, tool-makers, test pilots, and so forth. "Line troops" are the welders, riveters, machine operators, and mechanics.

Executives are the "senior officers," while the managers and supervisors are "junior officers." The foremen and their assistants are the "sergeants," and lead-men are the "corporals."

"Privates" and "privates-first-class" are the men who do the basic work, rated in accordance with their experience and ability.

Administration

The purpose of the administrative group in an aircraft factory is to secure contracts, make sure that the customers are satisfied, and decide on general policies which will enable the company to expand with the greatest speed and efficiency. It comprises company officers (that is, stockholders and board members), who decide on company policies, and executives who see that these policies are carried out.

1

Assisting the officers and executives are proportionate numbers of stenographers, accountants, typists, clerks, and timekeepers—whose essential duties resemble those of office workers in any factory.

Customer Representatives

Working closely with administrative and factory groups are the customer representatives, whose object in life is to assist the manufacturer in carrying out the terms of his contracts by means of inspection procedures and constructive criticism.

When the contract is for civilian or "commercial" aircraft, a single pilot or flight engineer may act as the customer representative. But the Army and Navy usually keep large staffs of specially trained civil-service personnel on hand at factories where government contracts are in effect. This is because civilian contracts are generally standardized and specific, whereas military contracts require constant alterations and changes.

An Army or Navy officer is the chief representative for the customer on government contracts, and his civil-service assistants are inspectors with good aeronautical backgrounds.

Experimental and Planning

In large aircraft factories, the experimental department is sometimes a small factory within itself. Its personnel includes the most highly skilled designers, mechanics, and engineering specialists the company can obtain. Their job is to develop the plans, create the improvements, build the models, and conduct the preliminary tests that make a prosperous and progressive aircraft factory possible. A thorough treatise on the functions of the experimental department will be found in Chapter 4.

Closely connected with the experimental department is the planning section—a group of experienced engineers, whose job is to transform the new ideas of the "experimenters" into the more practical realities of the assembly line. Here all drawings receive a final check for accuracy and vital cost estimates are made.

Production Engineering

In many aircraft factories, "Engineering" is the general title given to experimental, planning, and production sections as a whole. Distinctions are made here for purposes of clarity.

The general responsibility of the production engineering department is to take the estimates of the planning department along with the designs of the experimental department and supervise the actual building of airplanes. This may include tool designing, blueprint production, special processes, or anything that will enable the assembly lines to operate with maximum efficiency and economy.

Most engineers get their start as the result of special training in mechanical drawing or aerodynamics, but they rarely advance very far without a complete knowledge of aircraft construction and production methods.

Project Coordinators

Project coordinators are usually men of executive ability with a good general background in the aircraft industry. They are scattered throughout every department and branch of the entire factory, and their assignment is to handle all the miscellaneous problems that arise beyond the jurisdiction of regular department heads, supervisors, or foremen. This may include anything from finding a new type cotter pin to designing a more attractive letterhead for company stationery.

While project coordinators should have a good general knowledge of factory methods and procedure, their chief assets are intelligence and adaptability, rather than industrial technique. Good coordinators frequently become executives and company officers.

Plant Maintenance

Large aircraft factories today are virtually small cities, complete within themselves. They have their own lighting and plumbing systems, their own doctors and nurses, their own cafeterias, their own recreation departments, and even their own charitable organizations.

Therefore, some plants employ hundreds of nontechnical workers and professional men who have no specific knowledge of aviation. Such personnel comprise what is known as the plant maintenance group. Their job is to make the plant a safe, healthy, and desirable place for all the other employees.

Parts and Processes

The parts and processes section is where the manufacturing portion of the aircraft industry begins. Here all the hundreds of small elements that go to make up an airplane are received, processed, or constructed for transmission to primary assembly groups. Workmen of all types are employed in the parts and processes department, and this is generally considered the best place for a beginner to start learning the business.

First division of parts and processes is the receiving department, where all the materials—wood, metals, fabric, paint, radios, engines, armament, instruments, and so forth—are delivered by those manufacturers who act as supply agents for the aircraft industry. The materials received are ordered by the purchasing department, an organization of buyers operating directly with the planning and production engineering departments. Employees of the receiving department may be men of little previous experience; their job is to unpack parts for initial inspection, and then to distribute materials appropriately to all parts of the plant. These employees are known as stock clerks. The chief asset of a stock clerk is a good memory which will help him recall names, part numbers, and similar details.

The parts department is where the rivets, machine screws, nuts, bolts, turnbuckles, and other small yet vital parts of an airplane are fabricated. This work will be discussed with more detail in Chapter 6.

The chemical and testing laboratories are often as much a part of the experimental department as of the parts and processes section. They have three distinct functions:

(1) To develop new formulas and processes (for experimental).
(2) To test materials (for both departments).

(3) To make heat treatments, provide cadmium plating, accomplish anodizing, and so forth (for parts and processes).

Men with good elementary training in physics or chemistry are generally hired and trained by the company for jobs in the chemical and testing laboratories.

In the jigs, tools, and fixtures department (or departments) all the complicated tools and equipment needed for building airplanes are constructed. The toolmaker is the most important man in this section, and his pay is probably the highest of any workman in the industry. Other employees here include die-makers, welders, machine operators.

Primary Assembly

The primary-assembly section of an aircraft factory is where the major parts or sections of an airplane are made. The general subdivisions of this group are the fuselage (or hull) department, the wing department, tail assembly, engine build-up and assembly, the dope or paint department, the hydraulics section, the radio and electrical department, and the welding department.

Most numerous of the workers in primary assembly are the riveters, whose job is described in Chapter 7.

Since few aircraft factories build their own engines, engine build-up and assembly men are usually mechanics with special training at plants where engines are manufactured; their job is to assemble and install the power plant (including the engine, engine mount, accessories, and controls) in the airplane.

Modern aircraft factories may include a dope department, a paint department, or both—depending on the type of airplanes they manufacture. The paint department is usually confined to the protection of wood or metal parts with paint; the dope department deals entirely with parts covered by fabric. Either journeymen or apprentice painters may be employed at this type of work.

Hydraulics is a specialized science which has become of great importance to the aircraft industry in recent years; it deals with the

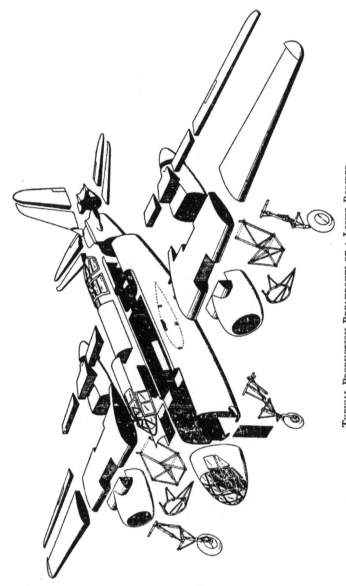

TYPICAL PRODUCTION BREAKDOWN OF A LIGHT BOMBER
(Douglas Aircraft Co. Photo)

operation of machinery by means of the controlled movements of liquids or fluids (such as light-grade oils). Hydraulic equipment may include anything from an ordinary jack, used in various assembly operations, to the intricate mechanism which raises and lowers the landing gear in a big transport plane. This equipment is usually purchased from outside manufacturers, and for this reason employees of the hydraulics department may be men with training beyond the confines of an airplane factory.

Next to toolmakers, welders are probably the best-paid workmen in an aircraft plant. Their training is long and hard, and they must pass rigid tests before they can work on even the smallest and most unimportant parts. A discussion of welding will be found in Chapter 7.

Almost any good electrician or radioman can get a job in the radio and electrical department of primary assembly. However, the new employee must immediately familiarize himself with airplane construction and installation methods.

Final Assembly

Final assembly is where the major parts of primary assembly are made into a finished airplane—sometimes on a moving assembly line. Here again the riveter plays a predominant role; but even more important is the tune-up mechanic, who gets the plane in shape for its initial flight. The latter is usually a man of long experience (a minimum of three years) with a Civil Aeronautics Authority license.

The two main divisions of final assembly are final finish, and final test and inspection.

In the final-finish division the construction work, painting, and so forth are completed. In final test and inspection, the airplane is tuned up and made ready for its initial flight.

Inspection

Like coordinators, inspectors are scattered throughout the plant—from parts and processes to final assembly. And their job is to make sure that every rivet, nut, bolt, joint, section, and part of an airplane will prove satisfactory. A complete description of the duties of aircraft inspectors will be found in Chapter 8.

Salvage

The salvage department comprises specially trained, experienced men whose job is to gather and save all the scrap metal, rejected parts, and other materials that can be used again after an airplane is finished. Since metal is generally the chief item salvaged, men in this department should know the fundamentals of metallurgy. A knowledge of aircraft construction and factory organization is also essential.

Flight Test and Service Departments

The flight test group of an airplane factory includes the expert pilots, flight engineers, radiomen, and special observers whose job is to fly and obtain performance data on standard as well as experimental aircraft. Although much has been written on the dangers encountered by the test pilot and his crew, these jobs are far more prosaic and technical than most literary men would have us believe. For every hour spent in the air, the flight experts spend at least five hours on the ground, studying and determining the ways and means of making their jobs and aviation as a whole as safe as possible. For this reason, many test pilots eventually become company officers or executives—and die of old age.

The service department of an airplane factory is closely coordinated with the flight test group. It comprises well-trained and efficient mechanics whose job is to repair and service airplanes after they have been test-flown and delivered to the customer. Spare parts and tools for this work are provided by the factory proper, and the operations of the service department frequently extend from the day an airplane is delivered until the time when it is finally "decommissioned."

Supported by a monorail crane, the fuselage of a huge **Flying Fortress** is moved to the final-assembly line, where it will soon become part of a finished airplane. (*Boeing Aircraft Co. Photo*)

Above. Fuselage sections for a big land bomber start down a moving final-assembly line. (*Consolidated Aircraft Corp. Photo*)

Below. Wings are attached to the fuselage of a B-17 Flying Fortress in a final-assembly operation. (*Boeing Aircraft Co. Photo*)

2

AERODYNAMICS

The science of aerodynamics is concerned largely with the study of airfoils. Airfoils are surfaces designed to secure useful reactions from the air, and the two main types are "lift" airfoils and "thrust" airfoils.

"Thrust" is the power which enables an airplane to move forward. "Lift" is a force aroused by thrust, which causes an airplane to rise from the surface of the earth.

In the conventional modern airplane, the wing is the lift airfoil and the propeller is the thrust airfoil.

The function of a wing is to produce or utilize lift by directing air currents in a useful manner over and under its surfaces, as shown in Figure 1.

FIG. 1. THE WING AS A LIFT AIRFOIL

The arrows in this drawing represent air currents. Note the vacuum they form over the upper surface, or "camber" of the wing; this vacuum is better known as lift. It literally sucks the wing away from the surface of the earth. Notice also that the wing is not level; the angle at which it points upward (or downward) is called "the angle of attack."

British airmen call the propeller an "airscrew," and this designa-

9

tion is more apt than most Americans would believe; for the function of a propeller is to twist its way through thin air—the same as
an ordinary screw would twist its way through a piece of wood. The
chief difference between a propeller and a wood screw is that a propeller has only a thin supporting medium (air) and allows considerable "slippage."

The first satisfactory development of a propeller resulted from
the "Blade Element Theory," introduced by a Polish scientist named
Drzewieski. It concluded that a propeller "consists of several airfoil
sections (blades) joined together side by side to form an airfoil
which will create thrust when revolving in a plane about a central
axis." This is illustrated in Figure 2.

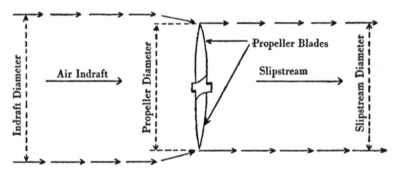

FIG. 2. THE PROPELLER AS A THRUST AIRFOIL

Air Forces

The air forces encountered and aroused by an airplane in flight
are generally classified as (1) lift forces, (2) drag forces, and (3)
side forces. The general tendencies of these forces are shown in Figure 3.

All forces act upon the "plane of symmetry" of an airplane. The
plane of symmetry is such that all of one side of an airplane is a
mirror image of the other side.

As stated previously, lift forces support the airplane and make flight possible. Drag forces resist forward motion and must be counteracted by propeller thrust. Side forces are normally symmetrical and neutralize one another.

Thus, it is said that an airplane flies in conformity with its lift-drag ratio. In other words, the airfoil producing lift, when combined with thrust, must be efficient enough to overcome the drag which is

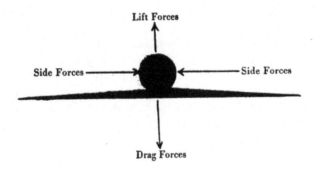

Lift Forces

Side Forces   Side Forces

Drag Forces

FIG. 3. GENERAL TENDENCIES OF AIR FORCES

produced by the fuselage and other parts that do not act as lift airfoils.

In certain special circumstances, it is possible for the fuselage or tail section of a conventional airplane to produce lift. But this is the exception, not the rule.

Physically, the aerodynamic forces aroused by lift and thrust airfoils are virtually the same as the "hydrodynamic" forces which govern an aquaplane. The aquaplane can support twice its own weight when pulled across water at a high rate of speed, but it sinks under such a load when standing still. Similarly, an airplane flies when its propeller produces thrust and slips earthward when the power is shut off. The difference between aerodynamic and hydrodynamic forces is purely a matter of supporting mediums, or water and air. Both water and air are fluids in the language of physical science, their primary distinctions being the fact that water weighs more than air.

The Davis and Northrup Wings

At this writing, the most efficient lift-producing airfoil in mass production is the Davis wing, a modification of which is part of the giant B-24 Liberator bomber.

The Davis wing is the result of a comparatively simple mathematical formula, which at the time of this writing is a military secret. It was developed in order to disprove the old theory that a thin, flat surface is the ideal airfoil; it has provided designers with a suitable means of developing airfoils from curves or circles. The original Davis wing was used on a multi-engined flying boat.

Every exterior projection—even a tiny rivet head—that is not specifically designed as an airfoil increases the drag tendencies of an airplane. To date no airplane has been designed so as to eliminate thoroughly the drag element, but the experimental Northrup "flying wing" seems close to this ideal.

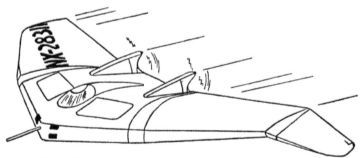

Fig. 4. The Northrup "Flying Wing," a Tailless Airplane
(Aero Digest)

The Northrup wing has no fuselage or tail section; all necessary compartments and controls are housed in a single lift airfoil. This eliminates drag, and thus increases flying efficiency.

The trouble with most tailless airplanes is the fact that they cannot be maneuvered satisfactorily. Special control surfaces have apparently solved many such difficulties in the Northrup design, and now it seems probable that flying wings may soon become conventional.

3

AIRCRAFT TYPES AND NOMENCLATURE

As a rule, military aircraft are classified according to usage while civilian aircraft are classified according to structure. For example, the huge Flying Fortresses are "B-17 bombers" to the Army; but to an airline they would simply be "multi-engined monoplanes."

Since structure is of most importance to the aircraft worker, the civilian method of classification will prevail in this book. However, everyone interested in aviation should know the following general designations employed by the United States Army and Navy:

Army Designations

A—Attack (Light Bomber)
AT—Advanced Trainer
B—Bomber
BT—Basic Trainer
C—Cargo (or Transport)
F—Photographic

L—Liaison
LB—Light Bomber
O—Observation
OA—Amphibian
P—Pursuit (Fighter)
PB—Pursuit Interceptor (Optional)
X—Experimental

Navy Designations

B—Bombing
BT—Bombing-Torpedo
F—Fighting
H—Ambulance (or Hospital)
J—Utility
JR—Utility-Transport
L—Glider

N—Training
O—Observation
OS—Observation-Scouting
P—Patrol
PB—Patrol-Bombing
R—Transport (also G)
S—Scouting

13

SB—Scouting-Bombing	T—Torpedo
SN—Scout Training	TB—Torpedo-Bombing
SO—Scouting-Observation	X—Experimental
	ZN—Airship (nonrigid)

Specific Army airplanes are usually designated only by one of the above letters and a model number—such as "P-38," which indicates a Model Number 38 Pursuit Plane. However, improved versions of Army aircraft models may be indicated by additional letters—such as "B-24D," "B-17E," and so forth.

Theoretically, each Navy aircraft designation should be preceded by the letter "V" (meaning heavier-than-air), or the letter "Z" (meaning lighter-than-air). But such prefixes are rarely employed in airplane factories. Usually a type symbol, a manufacturer's symbol, and a model number will suffice. Thus, when we hear someone speak of a "PBY-5," we know he is talking about a Patrol Bomber (PB) built by the Consolidated Aircraft Corporation (Y), Model Number 5.

By way of comparison, the general classifications used by the Civil Aeronautics Authority are:

Class 1—Single-engined airplane with gross weight of not more than 1300 lbs.

Class 2S—Single-engined airplane with gross weight of 1300–1400 lbs.

Class 2M—Multi-engined airplane with gross weight of 1300–1400 lbs.

Class 3S—Single-engined airplane with gross weight of 4000–10,000 lbs.

Class 3M—Multi-engined airplane with gross weight of 4000–10,000 lbs.

Class 4S—Single-engined airplane with gross weight of over 10,000 lbs.

Class 4M—Multi-engined airplane with gross weight of over 10,000 lbs.

General Construction Characteristics

The conventional modern airplane has four main parts: (1) the power plant, which produces thrust; (2) the wing, which gives lift;

(3) the fuselage, or hull, which houses the cargo and crew; (4) the tail section, which may provide either stability or maneuverability. It is therefore only natural for airplane construction types to be in conformity with the design characteristics or purposes of these component parts.

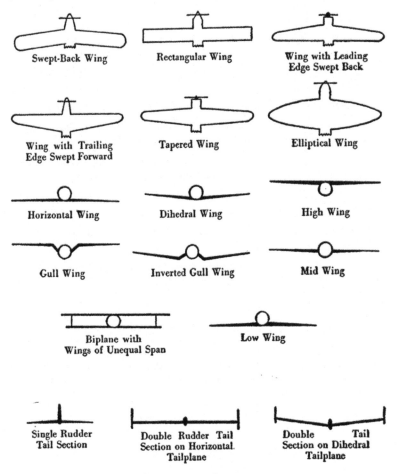

Swept-Back Wing   Rectangular Wing   Wing with Leading Edge Swept Back

Wing with Trailing Edge Swept Forward   Tapered Wing   Elliptical Wing

Horizontal Wing   Dihedral Wing   High Wing

Gull Wing   Inverted Gull Wing   Mid Wing

Biplane with Wings of Unequal Span   Low Wing

Single Rudder Tail Section   Double Rudder Tail Section on Horizontal Tailplane   Double Tail Section on Dihedral Tailplane

FIG. 5. CONSTRUCTION CHARACTERISTICS

Hence, the National Advisory Committee for Aeronautics (N.A.C.A.) is able to list the following general airplane types:

Amphibian: An airplane designed to rise from and alight on either land or water.

Biplane: An airplane with two main supporting surfaces (wings) placed one above another.

Flying Boat: A form of seaplane supported, when resting on the surface of water, by a hull or hulls providing flotation in addition to serving as fuselages. For the central hull type, lateral stability is usually provided by wing-tip floats.

Landplane: An airplane designed to rise from and alight on land.

Monoplane: An airplane which has but one supporting surface (wing), sometimes divided into two parts by the fuselage.

Multiplane: An airplane with two or more main supporting surfaces (wings), placed one above another. This term is used infrequently.

Pusher Airplane: An airplane with the propeller or propellers in the rear of the main supporting surfaces.

Quadruplane: An airplane with four main supporting surfaces (wings), placed one above another.

Seaplane: Any airplane designed to rise from and alight on the water. This general term applies to both boat and float types, though the boat type is usually designated as a "flying boat."

Ship-plane: A landplane designed to rise from and alight on the deck of a ship. This is another term rarely used, the more popular designation being "carrier plane."

Tandem Airplane: An airplane with two or more sets of wings of substantially the same area (not including the tail unit) placed one in front of the other and on about the same level.

Tractor Airplane: An airplane with the propeller or propellers forward of the main supporting surfaces.

Triplane: An airplane with three supporting surfaces (wings), placed one above another.

Other aircraft construction features generally mentioned are:

(1) Over-all dimensions (length, height, etc.).
(2) Weight (minimum and maximum).
(3) Landing gear (retractable or stationary).
(4) Number of hull steps (in flying boats or amphibians).
(5) Cockpit locations (enclosed or open).

Stationing

"Stationing" is the system used by airplane manufacturers to identify or locate parts of an airplane. Stations are numbered according to their distance from the nose of the ship in the fuselage or tail sections, or according to their distance from the centerline of the fuselage in the wing section. These distances are generally stated in terms of inches.

For example, station *0* on any airplane would be either the foremost part of the fuselage or the very center of the wing; a bulkhead or spar thirty inches from either of these points would be station *30*, and so forth. (See Figure 6.)

Power-Plant Nomenclature

The power plant of an airplane generally comprises an engine and a propeller. In large airplanes, however, this term may also designate the "auxiliary power unit"—a small gasoline engine used to operate auxiliary motors or to charge batteries.

Most modern airplane engines are either air cooled or water cooled, and resemble the gasoline-fed types popular in motorcycles and automobiles. Their size and power depend upon the requirements of the individual airplanes.

Propellers are classified according to the "pitch properties" of their respective blades. Pitch is the angle at which a propeller blade is placed on the propeller hub in order to produce thrust (see Glossary). Thus, a "fixed pitch" propeller has blades set for the most effective thrust in normal circumstances; its simplicity and economical features make it practicable for light planes. A "variable (or controllable) pitch" propeller has blades that can be turned in flight for maximum operating efficiency at all times; it is most frequently used in the big multi-engined airplanes.

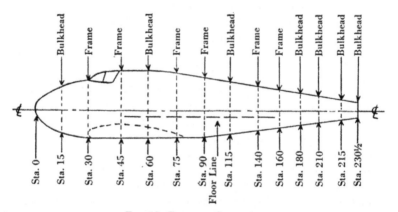

FIG. 6A. FUSELAGE STATIONING

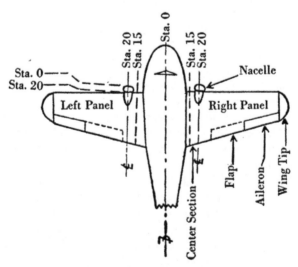

FIG. 6B. WING STATIONING

The power-plant housing is usually the forepart of the fuselage in a single-engined airplane, or nacelles set in the leading edge of the wing of a multi-engined airplane.

Separating the power plant from the airplane proper is a firewall, ordinarily made of stainless steel. The power plant is streamlined and protected by metal cowling, which may also include "cowl flaps" if the engine is air cooled. Cowl flaps encircle the air-cooled motor, and their purpose is to control cylinder-head temperatures by enabling the pilot to increase or decrease the flow of air inside the cowling.

Surface Controls

The conventional modern airplane is navigated or guided through the air by a series of auxiliary airfoils commonly known as surface controls. Briefly, these include rudders, elevators, ailerons, trimming tabs, and sometimes "wing flaps."

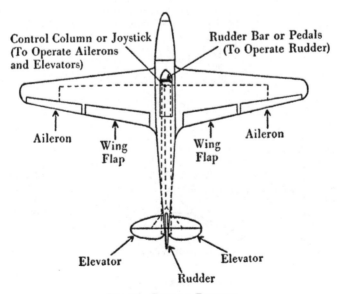

Fig. 7A. Control Diagram

The rudder provides directional control (as in a boat), and is attached to the vertical stabilizer in the tail section. The elevators provide longitudinal control (for diving or climbing), and are attached to the horizontal stabilizer in the tail section. The ailerons, working in opposite directions, provide lateral control (for banking or roll-

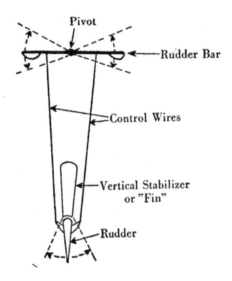

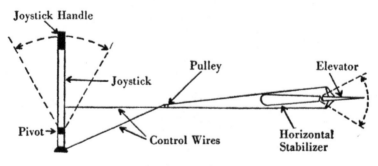

Fig. 7B. Control Diagrams

ing), and are attached to the trailing edges of the wing. Trimming tabs are tiny, movable surfaces built in the other controls respectively; their purpose is to enable the pilot to trim his plane for level flight without moving the main controls from the neutral position. Sometimes called "air brakes," wing flaps are surfaces situated between the ailerons and fuselage and designed so they can be moved in or out of the trailing edge of the wing; they may either decrease the speed of the airplane for diving or landing, or increase the wing area for added lift on a take-off.

A joystick, or control column, in the pilot's cockpit operates both the ailerons and elevators; a rudder bar, or foot pedals, moves the rudder. The tabs are set by a special group of hand controls, and the wing flaps are operated hydraulically.

Wing Nomenclature

The three general wing types are:

(1) Externally braced.
(2) Externally and internally braced.
(3) Internally braced.

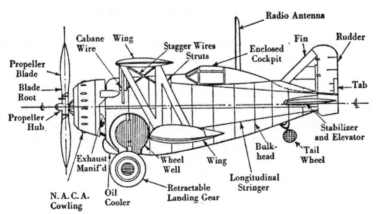

Fig. 8A. Grumman Biplane Nomenclature

Rapidly becoming obsolete in the United States, the externally braced wing is typified by the biplane (see Figure 8A). The external bracing generally comprises struts and wires, designed to strengthen the wings without greatly increasing the drag element.

More popular is the wing braced both internally and externally, called the semicantilever type. This is a monoplane wing, partly braced against the fuselage by two or more struts.

The most widely used design at present is the wing braced internally, known as the full cantilever type. Improved airfoils and

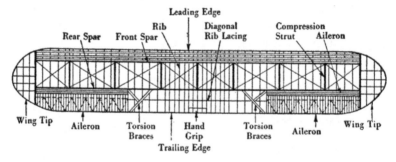

FIG. 8B. "TYPICAL" WING NOMENCLATURE

advanced engineering have made this design possible, and its general superiority is recognized throughout the industry. It is also a monoplane wing.

Structurally speaking, a wing usually comprises a series of metal ribs, connected by horizontal metal spars and covered by a "skin" of alclad sheet metal or fabric treated with "dope" or lacquer. The external or internal bracing, of course, depends upon the size and type of wing.

In many airplanes, fuel and oil tanks are incorporated in the center section of the wing. Also part of this structure are the aileron and wing-flap controls, landing lights (in the leading edge), and sometimes power-plant nacelles and controls (in multi-engined aircraft).

Some of the intricate mechanism of a modern variable-pitch propeller can be seen in this F4U-1 Corsair. Gears to turn the propeller blades are situated inside the propeller "boss." (*Vought-Sikorsky Aircraft Photo*)

Above. Ribs are connected by spars to form the wing framework of a light airplane. (*Piper Aircraft Corp. Photo*)

Below. Workmen are attaching stationary landing gear to the fuselage of a light trainer plane. Note how part of the landing-gear load is carried by a "stub wing strut" and wires to the fuselage. (*Ryan Aeronautical Co. Photo*)

Fuselage Nomenclature

With the exception of a few experimental designs, the monocoque (or "eggshell") type fuselage is used in all modern American airplanes. This type may be divided into three classes—reinforced shell, semimonocoque, and full monocoque—and a single fuselage may include sections in each of these classes.

Succinctly, the monocoque type fuselage comprises a thin skin of metal, supported by a framework of metal parts so disposed as to carry the stresses to which the structure may be subjected. In the reinforced shell class, the skin is supported by a complete framework of structural members (that is, bulkheads, stringers, longerons, etc.). In the semimonocoque class, the skin is reinforced by longerons and vertical bulkheads, but has no diagonal web members. In the full monocoque class, the skin is reinforced only by vertical bulkheads or "fuselage rings."

Strong aluminum alloys, and sometimes steel, are generally used for the fuselage framework; the exterior covering, or "skin," is frequently either alclad sheet metal or doped fabric. For further information on materials, see Chapter 5.

The most important part of the fuselage is the pilot's compartment or cockpit. Here all the instruments, controls, and radio equipment are installed; it is the nerve center of the entire airplane. Other parts of the fuselage may include cargo space or living compartments for the passengers or crew, depending on the size and purpose of the airplane.

Tail Sections

The tail section of the conventional modern airplane is built up around the tail cone of the fuselage. It comprises stabilizers, designed to balance the airplane, and the previously described surface controls.

The two types of stabilizers are "horizontal" and "vertical," and they are fixed to the tail cone so that they cannot be moved. Their

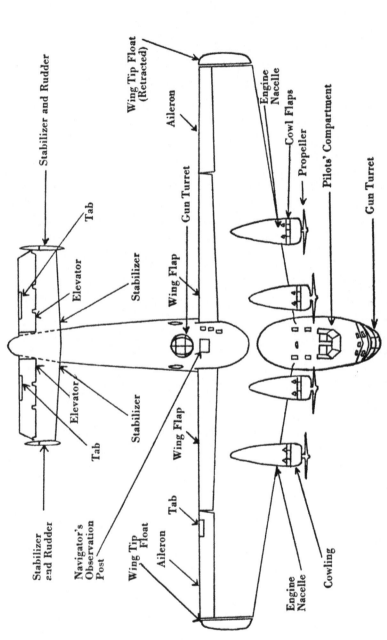

FIG. 9A. NOMENCLATURE OF THE FLYING BOAT (CONSOLIDATED PB2Y CORONADO)

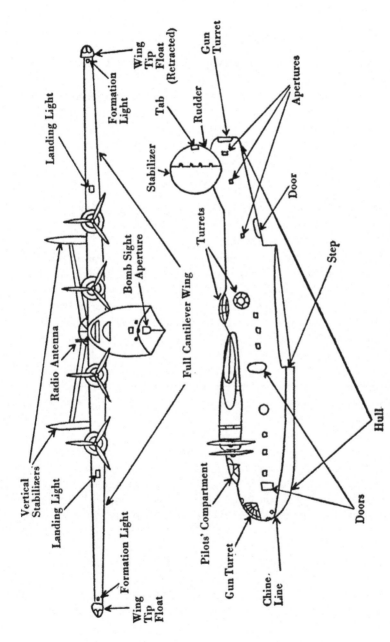

FIG. 9B. NOMENCLATURE OF THE FLYING BOAT (CORONADO)

framework is of the cantilever type, covered by the regular fuselage "skin."

Affixed to the horizontal and vertical stabilizers, respectively, are elevators and rudders. Their structure is also said to be of the cantilever type. However, fabric is more generally used as skin on surface controls, since fabric-covered surfaces are comparatively light and less apt to flutter while the airplane is in flight.

Landing Gear Nomenclature

The landing gear of an airplane is generally considered part of the fuselage. However, its function is so distinct—and important—that it merits special attention.

There are two types of landing gear in everyday use at present. The so-called "standard" type consists of two main wheels just ahead of the airplane's center of gravity, usually affixed to the lower part of the fuselage or underneath the wing, and a small wheel or skid affixed to the tail cone; this type of landing gear causes the nose of the airplane to point upward when the airplane is parked on the ground. Comparatively new, but rapidly gaining popularity, is the "tricycle" type landing gear, which comprises two main wheels just behind the airplane's center of gravity, extending from the lower part of a fuselage or wing, and a somewhat smaller wheel extending from the nose of the fuselage.

Proponents claim that the tricycle landing gear prevents accidents such as ground loops, making it easier for a pilot to take off and land. This type is becoming especially popular in heavy airplanes.

Any type of landing gear may be either retractable or stationary. Retractable gear has wheels attached to "oleo struts" which can be retracted or withdrawn into wheel wells in the fuselage or wing of an airplane in flight; shock is absorbed by the hydraulic mechanism that operates the gear when landing. Stationary landing gear has wheels attached to fixed or immovable struts with shock cord, or something similar, to help absorb the impact of landing.

Being most economical and safest for inexperienced pilots, stationary landing gear is popular in light planes when speed is not essential. Retractable landing gear eliminates the drag produced by stationary landing gear and is used in commercial and military planes when utmost flying efficiency is essential.

Seaplanes, Flying Boats, and Amphibians

As has been explained previously, a "seaplane" technically is any airplane equipped to take off from and land on water. However, this term generally designates a standard fuselage airplane equipped with floats instead of landing gear.

An airplane with a hull, rather than a fuselage, is called a "flying boat"; if it has a landing gear along with a hull or floats, and can operate from either land or water, it is an amphibian.

The chief difference between a fuselage and a hull is the fact that the latter has a keel, like that of a motorboat. This keel is so shaped and constructed as to present the most internal strength and the least external resistance to water, rather than air; it comprises the lower part of the hull. The upper part of the hull is constructed along the general lines of a regular monocoque fuselage.

The keel of a flying boat differs from the keel of an ordinary boat in that it has one or more "steps." A step is a sharp break in the lower rear portion of the keel; its purpose is to break the grip of the water on the keel when the flying boat is taking off. A step is said to be "ventilated" when it includes an air hole to prevent the formation of a vacuum between the keel and the water; ventilated steps are sometimes used on large, multi-engined flying boats.

An amphibian may include either a hull or floats along with landing gear that is retractable. It is perhaps the most difficult of all airplane types to design and build, owing to the fact that amphibious structures are conducive to leaks; also, it is difficult to find landing gear materials which will effectively resist the corrosive effects of salt water.

4

AIRCRAFT DESIGN PRINCIPLES

When an aircraft manufacturer wants to build a new airplane, his first step is to decide precisely what is most needed. Then, for the benefit of his designer, he draws up a list of specifications which state definitely:

(1) The airplane type and purpose.

(2) The required performance (take-off and landing speeds, rate of climb, maximum range, etc.).

(3) The disposable load (with allowances for crew and passengers, fuel and oil, equipment, etc.).

(4) The required structural strength.

(5) General requirements regarding cost of materials, ease of production, etc.

(6) Special requirements as to details to be incorporated in the design.

From this, the designer can determine almost at once what his airplane is going to look like; but he does not even begin to put his ideas on paper until he has visited the plant library and obtained all the information available regarding the type of airplane called for by the specifications. This eliminates from the start much needless experimentation and guesswork. Then the compromises begin.

Every airplane is said to be the result of a series of compromises. Size (or weight) must sometimes be sacrificed for cost; maximum speeds often are sacrificed for safer and lower landing speeds; stability may be sacrificed for maneuverability.

The first concrete step in designing an airplane is choosing an engine. In factories that build their own engines, this may be a comparatively simple matter; but generally the designer is limited in his choice by considerations of price, servicing facilities, and availability. If alternate engines are available, the early stages of the design are usually carried out so that any one of them may be used.

A low-powered engine requires less fuel and oil—thus decreasing the weight of the airplane, the area of the wing, and the size of the fuselage. On the other hand, a high-powered engine may entail such an increase in sizes and weights and areas that it is economically impractical because the resulting performance will not justify the cost.

Choosing an Airfoil Section

Since the construction of a propeller is, like the construction of an engine, a highly specialized business, most aircraft manufacturers buy such airfoils complete from outside sources; but the choice of a wing is another matter. The ideal wing should have the following characteristics:

(1) High maximum lift.
(2) Low drag value.
(3) Lightness without a sacrifice of strength.

Naturally, it is impossible to incorporate all the most desirable features in every wing design. For example, thin airfoil sections normally show a lower drag coefficient than thick ones; yet, if the airplane under consideration happens to be a cantilever monoplane, considerable depth is necessary to allow for internal bracing. Therefore, the designer must again refer to his library data—which should include a list of all the various types of airfoil sections that have been developed—then select the airfoil section he considers best suited to his purposes.

General wing dimensions are next determined, after which the designer is ready to begin putting his ideas on paper. His first drawing is usually a side elevation of the airplane, showing the fuselage stations. The order of the contents of the fuselage depends largely on the function for which the airplane is designed; seats and equipment must be distributed so as to provide a fixed center of gravity plus maximum convenience and comfort for the passengers and crew.

With the side view complete, the designer is able to make up a "balance schedule"—which will determine the airplane's center of gravity and enable him to place his wing correctly. Also from this, he can ascertain the areas required in his tail section. Then he makes a finished three-view drawing.

Wind-Tunnel Tests

Performance charts and other library data will give the designer some idea of how his airplane will perform at this stage. But there is only one way to be certain, and that is to build a model which can be tested in a wind tunnel. A wind tunnel is a chamber in which artificial winds can be created, so as to determine an airplane's reaction to thrust.

Part of the experimental department of every large aircraft factory is a model shop, the purpose of which is to build small yet extremely accurate and true-to-scale models of proposed airplanes. Designers generally find that models perform better than the finished product. This is because there are so many small drag-producing elements (wires, struts, and so forth) in a big plane that cannot be reproduced in models. However, with reasonable allowances, fairly close performance statistics can be obtained from wind-tunnel models; and, if these statistics are not satisfactory, the designer must scrap his plans and start all over again.

Mock-up

Since it is economically impractical to build a full-sized airplane (the merits of which are still in doubt) from drawings alone, the next step is to construct a full-sized model from wood. This is called the mock-up.

Usually the mock-up represents the fuselage from the nose to the tail section, but only the center section and one side of a wing. It is constructed by specially trained carpenters in the wood shop of the experimental department. All the more important structural members are included in the mock-up, and parts such as engines are represented by wooden dummies made to scale. The completed model is usually covered with paper, rough canvas, or plywood.

The mock-up enables the designer and his assistants to visualize more thoroughly the completed airplane. Consequently, changes in arrangement at this point are frequent.

Final acceptance of the mock-up marks the end of the first phase of the design of an airplane. The wind-tunnel tests have proved that the airplane will perform satisfactorily from the standpoints of stability and controllability, and the mock-up has proved that the structure is practical from the standpoints of engineering and convenience for the passengers and crew.

Stress Analysis

The second phase of aircraft design begins with the answer to the question of whether the airplane structure will be able to withstand the forces to which it will be subjected. This is stress analysis.

Generally speaking, the forces which an airplane must withstand are as follows:

(1) Weight and inertia forces.
(2) Air forces.
(3) Ground reactions.
(4) Engine and propeller forces.
(5) Reactions between structural members.

"Weight and inertia forces" are the result of gravity, which constantly tends to pull the airplane toward the center of the earth. The magnitude of the pull depends on the size of the airplane.

"Air forces" are the pressure exerted on the exterior of the airplane by the various air currents created and encountered in flight, as have previously been described in the chapter on Aerodynamics. The amount of pressure depends on the size, shape, and speed of the airplane.

"Ground reactions" are the forces brought to bear when the airplane stops flying and lands. The extent of these forces depends on the landing speed of the airplane, its size, and the shock-absorbing capacities of the landing gear.

"Engine and propeller forces" account for the strain placed on the airplane structure by the vibrations, movements, and weight of the engine and propeller.

"Reactions between structural members" include the capacity of one part of an airplane to assume some of the forces placed upon another part. Since the external forces on an airplane in flight are rarely well distributed, it is important that unloaded parts be capable of supplementing or strengthening parts that are under stress.

Detailed Design

With his library data, and by means of special laboratory tests, the designer can calculate with almost minute accuracy the forces his airplane will encounter in flight. Then he comes to the business of making a detailed design, which will give his airplane the strength to resist any and all of the forces mentioned above.

The first step here is to consult the Civil Aeronautics Authority "Airworthiness" regulations (see the Bibliography), to ascertain the minimum structural requirements of the government. And at this point the designer begins dealing with "factors."

First up for consideration is the "ultimate-load factor," which designates the strain a part must withstand without failing. Then there is the "yield factor," which determines the amount of deflection a part will withstand without being permanently distorted. And, in addition, a "safety factor" must be considered.

The safety factor decrees that no structural part of an airplane shall at any time be subjected to more than two-thirds its maximum load or yield capacities.

With all factors considered, the designer completes his general structural drawings and calls in the drafting department. Before actual construction work can begin, detail drawings must be made —showing the location, size, and material of every significant and insignificant part that will go into the finished airplane.

These drawings—which may number thousands for a single design

Above. At work in the drafting room, where frequently all may be simultaneously engaged in making drawings for a single airplane. (*Douglas Aircraft Co. Photo*)

Below. The loft floor is shown here in the foreground of the engineering department. (*Lockheed Aircraft Corp. Photo*)

These men are studying "production illustrations." Frequently referred to as "ABC drawings," the illustrations tell the worker every step to make and the proper sequence of operations from the beginning through to the finished assembly. (*Boeing Aircraft Co. Photo*)

—are issued to the workmen when the designer is convinced they are sufficient and complete. Then the "lofting" of a "prototype" airplane can be completed.

The prototype is the initial full-scale flying model, and its construction is often a lengthy and costly proceeding. All parts must be handmade because the manufacturer cannot afford the complicated and expensive jigs necessary for mass production before the prototype has been built and flown satisfactorily.

Lofting

Lofting is where designing ends and construction begins; it consists of laying out the parts of an airplane full-size on a "loft floor" and necessitates the following types of work:

(1) Lines showing the shape of fuselage, hull, wings, tail section.

(2) Assembly boards (from which work may begin).

(3) Templates for layout, drill, and trimming.

(4) Form blocks (of wood or metal, forming two-way curvatures).

(5) Flat patterns.

At one time the practice was to convey all engineering information by means of blueprints, which recorded the necessary sizes and shapes on paper—usually at less than full scale. But the consequent shop interpretations frequently led to serious difficulties. Lofting was therefore adopted as the simplest, most direct method of transmitting much of the required data.

Lofting starts with preliminary design. The beam, over-all length, height, and other dimensions are first determined; then a small-scale drawing showing the desired shape is made for the hull. Next, centerline drawings of the wing structural parts—such as bulkheads, beltframes, and keel—are made and structural sizes determined.

From this the lofting department is able to lay out and fair a full-sized body plan—including vertical sections, horizontal sections, longitudinal sections, and any diagonals or special sections necessary to make a completely faired job. Tolerances here are .005 inch or less.

The lofting department then lifts the contour of any part from the master body plan and puts it on a shop layout board. Lofting is done on boards or metal; the material used is given a coat of flat white

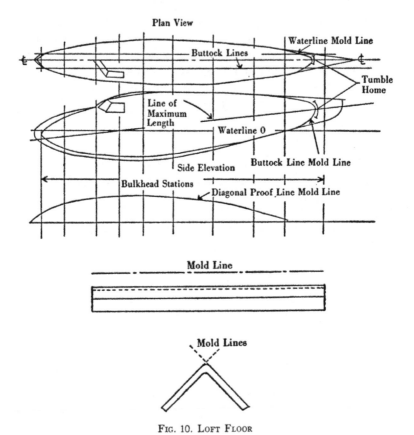

FIG. 10. LOFT FLOOR

paint so the lines will show up clearly. The contour is taken from the master body plan, after which the structural members are drawn on the layout board. From this layout, drill templates showing the locations of all rivets and bolts are made. When locating fixtures are needed, the lofting department notifies the tool design department so that tools will be ready when required.

In addition to this work, the lofting department furnishes contours for all bumping forms, templates that are required by the shop, master layouts required by the shop, master layouts required by tool design, and templates for outside-procured parts.

Following are words common to loft, layout, and template nomenclature:

Loft floor—usually a large wooden table upon which full-sized layouts are made. The lines for each model are cut into the surface of the table; then, when all necessary data are obtained, the lines are filled and sanded smooth, leaving a clean surface for the next model.

Body plan—a view looking forward, showing all frames or stations.

Mold line (ML)—the theoretical line formed by the intersection of two surfaces, such as the external edge of frames, stringers, etc.

Buttock line (BL)—an edge view of a vertical plane through a body; the centerline of the body in the plan view is taken as buttock line *0*. The planes of all other buttock lines are then parallel to the vertical centerline plane.

Waterline (WL)—an edge view of a horizontal plane through a body. The base line of the body is taken as waterline *0*. The planes of waterlines are parallel to the horizontal base-line plane.

Base line—a line from which the stations of an airplane are dimensioned.

Diagonal proof line (DPL)—an edge view of a diagonal plane through a body. These diagonal planes are passed through the body as a final check on fairness, or to fair portions of the body which undergo abrupt changes of contour.

Tumble home—the abrupt change of curvature of a mold line, buttock line, or waterline contour at the ends of the contour.

Scrieve-board layout (SB Layout)—a sheet of wood or metal upon which the results of various lofting operations are recorded in the form of contours and other measurable lines.

Master template (MST)—a template upon which are shown all contours for a particular section of an airplane—such as the horizontal stabilizer rib contours.

Angle template (AT)—made by bending a piece of template stock into an angle; used for laying out rivet locations, cutouts, etc., on extruded sections.

Block template (BT)—used to determine the exact size and shape of form blocks made from steel, zinc, or wood. Joggles and angles are given on block templates; angles are noted as to whether bends are up or down.

Contour template (CT)—used for checking contours of form blocks, spinning blocks, wood patterns (standard scale), and finished parts.

Drill template (DT)—made with hardened steel bushings or plates attached to act as guides for drilling holes.

Drill-jig template (DJT)—used for locating drill bushings on drill jigs and may be made either from engineering or tool-design drawings.

Flat template (FT)—also called layout template; is a developed flat pattern for laying out parts by hand or blanking and piercing dies. It may show bend dies if the part is to be formed on the brake, but if formed over a block the bend lines are usually omitted.

Gage template (GT)—used for checking finished widths of bent-up sections, such as flanged spars. It is also used for checking purchased parts or material.

Marking template (MT)—made to fit extruded sections or odd shapes; used for marking end cuts and cutouts.

Master router template (MRT)—large templates fastened to plywood; used for locating router patterns on material and as guides for the drilling of pilot holes and pin holes.

Nibbler template (NT)—made from heavy sheet stock or tubing; used as a guide for the nibbler in making peculiarly shaped cuts.

Profile template (PT)—made only for special router setups.

Router template (RT)—fastened to masonite or plywood; used as guides for cutting out sheet metal on the router. They are sometimes made $\frac{7}{32}$ undersize to accommodate the width of the guide used with the router cutter.

Stock template (ST)—similar to a flat template, except that it often has to be developed by hit-or-miss methods. Templates for blanks used on the hydro press or drop hammer are frequently in this classification.

$\frac{1}{8}$ *Shrink template* ($\frac{1}{8}$ ST)—is laid out with $\frac{1}{8}$ shrink scale; used in making patterns for drop-hammer dies.

Trim template (TT)—used as a guide for the trimming of parts after they have been formed on the drop hammer or in any case where a blank part cannot be cut accurately to size before forming. The trim template is often made directly from a drop-hammer part or from a piece of metal which has been formed over a part made on the drop hammer or hydro press.

5

MATERIALS AND PROCESSES

Aluminum and its alloys are the most important materials currently used in the aircraft industry. However, this predominance is by no means unchallenged.

Beryllium at present looms as the number one contender for top honors. Thirty per cent lighter than aluminum, it is comparatively easy to produce—and in some respects it is stronger than steel. However, for the moment, it remains in a more or less experimental stage.

Another metal that shows infinite promise is magnesium. Also lighter than aluminum, it is plentiful and easy to work. Recent developments in the welding of magnesium have increased its value at least 50 per cent; but the problems of making it fire and corrosion resistant cause it, temporarily at least, to remain in the background.

In the field of light airplanes, plastics apparently have the most brilliant future. Already several "all-plastic" airplanes have been "cooked"—and the feasibility of their use in nonmilitary aircraft has been proved beyond a doubt.

Steels, with their tremendous strength, have long played an important role in the business of building airplanes—and probably will continue to do so for a considerable time to come. And virtually the same thing can be said of "doped" fabric.

But these are by no means all the aircraft materials that are being used or show promise. A more complete and detailed description of such materials will be presented later in this chapter. Meanwhile, some attention to the subject of metallurgy is essential.

Metallurgy

All metals are listed under one of two different types: ferrous or nonferrous. Ferrous metals are iron and iron alloys, basically. Nonferrous metals are basically aluminum, copper, brass, nickel, and so forth, although they may be alloyed with iron.

Metals are identified by their physical properties. These may be listed as follows:

Hardness—the property of resisting penetration or permanent distortion. The hardness of most metals can be increased by hammering, rolling, or stretching; this is called "work-hardening." Steel and various other metals (including some aluminum alloys) can be further hardened by "heat treatment," a process that will be explained later.

Brittleness—the property of resisting a change in the relative position of molecules, or the tendency to break without a change in shape. Brittleness and hardness are closely associated. Hard material is always more brittle than soft material. In aircraft construction, the use of brittle material should be generally avoided; otherwise, shock resulting from the loads to which it will be subjected will cause failure.

Malleability—the property which allows some metals to be bent or permanently distorted without a rupture. It is the exact opposite of brittleness. This property permits the manufacture of sheets, bar stock, and forgings; also, it allows fabrication by bending and hammering.

Ductility—the property of metals which allows them to be drawn or deformed *severely* without breaking. This is necessary in the manufacture of wire, tubing, etc. It is a property similar to malleability; sometimes the two terms are used synonymously.

Elasticity—the property which enables a piece of metal to snap back into its original shape after being bent or distorted. All aircraft structural design is based on this property, since it would not be desirable to have any member remain permanently distorted after being subjected to a load. Each material has a point known as the elastic limit, beyond which it cannot be loaded without causing permanent distortion. This was discussed as a "yield factor" in Chapter 4.

Density—the weight of a unit volume of any material as compared with the weight of the same volume of water. In aircraft work, the actual weight of a material per cubic inch is often preferred, since this figure can be used in calculating the weight of a part before it is made. Density is best known as "specific gravity." It is calculated by using water (which weighs 62.3 pounds per cubic foot) as the figure "1," or basis of comparison. Thus, mercury (with a weight of 849 pounds per cubic foot) would have a density or specific gravity of 13.59—the ratio of its weight as compared with a similar volume of water. (For table of specific gravity, see the Appendix.)

Fusibility—the property of being liquefied by heat. All metals are fused in welding—steels at about 2500° F., and aluminum alloys at about 1100° F.

Conductivity—the power of transmitting cold, heat, or electricity. The conductivity of a metal is of interest to the welder as it affects the amount of heat he must use and, to a certain extent, the design of his welding jig. Electrical conductivity is also important in connection with the bonding of airplanes to eliminate radio interference and static electricity.

Toughness—the resistance of a metal to breaking after its elastic limit is passed. This is another opposite to brittleness.

Melting point—the temperature at which a material turns from its solid state to a liquid state. Tungsten and platinum are metals with a relatively high melting point; lead and zinc have comparatively low melting points.

Contraction and expansion—caused by the cooling or heating of metals. These properties may have a decided effect when an airplane is ascending from a low to a high altitude, or vice versa, throwing metal controls out of line and making various mechanisms hard to operate. Also, they must be carefully calculated by the welder.

Metallurgical Tests

The physical properties of metals are usually determined by what are known as "stress and strain" methods. In an aircraft factory, this is usually accomplished in the test laboratory for the experimental and other departments.

The following definitions should clarify the nature and objectives of such tests:

Stress—the load acting on a material. Internal stresses are the loads present in a material that has been strain-hardened; or in a casting as a result of shrinking by nonuniform cooling; or in a metal that has been heat-treated as the result of a rapid quench.

Tensile strength—generally referred to as the "ultimate tensile strength" (U.T.S.), is the maximum tensile load per square inch which a material can withstand. It is computed by dividing the maximum load obtained in a tensile test by the original cross-sectional area of the test specimen—the result being recorded in terms of pounds per square inch.

Elastic limit—the greatest load per square inch of original cross-sectional area which a material can withstand without permanent deformation. This must be determined by a series of tests.

Proof stress—the load per square inch a material can withstand without permanent elongation of more than .0001 inch per inch of gage length after complete release of stress. With the standard 2-inch gage length, the total allowable elongation would normally be .0002 inch.

Yield strength—the load per square inch at which a material exhibits a marked permanent set or elongation. This load is a fairly easily determined figure, and is commonly used.

Yield point—the load per square inch at which there occurs a marked increase in deformation without an increase in load. Only a few materials have a definite yield point; steel is one of these.

Strain—the deformation of material caused by an applied load.

The methods of making physical tests will be discussed in Chapter 8.

Heat Treatment

Technically, heat treatment is a chemical process whereby metals are refined and hardened. But, in a more general sense, this term may also designate the annealing, carburizing, case-hardening, and normalizing processes.

The full-solution heat treatment, or the strictly technical process, is as follows:

(1) The metal is heated to the temperature required to form a complete solid solution or absorption of all the alloying constituents into the basic metal crystals. This is done in a bath of molten sodium nitrate or a half-and-half mixture of sodium and potassium nitrate, contained in a gas-heated steel tank, or in an electrically heated air furnace. The material is held at the required temperature long enough for a complete blending of the alloying elements, then is cooled quickly by quenching—generally in cold water.

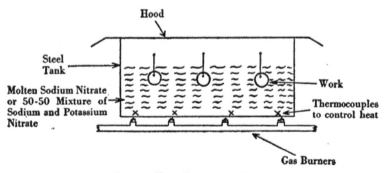

FIG. 11. HEAT-TREATMENT TANK

(2) The alloy is hardened and strengthened by reprecipitation or "aging." In some metals, this is accomplished by leaving them inert at room temperature for three or four days. Other metals must be artificially aged by heating to temperatures of around 300° F. for several hours.

The lengths of time and temperatures required to heat-treat various aluminum alloys are shown in the accompanying tables.

TIME REQUIRED IN HEAT-TREATING ALUMINUM ALLOYS
17S, 24S, 25S, AND 53S

THICKNESS OF MATERIAL (Inches)	TIME IN MINUTES Minimum	Maximum
Up to .020	5	15
.020 to $\frac{1}{32}$	10	20
$\frac{1}{32}$ to $\frac{1}{16}$	15	30
$\frac{1}{16}$ to $\frac{1}{8}$	20	40
$\frac{1}{8}$ to $\frac{1}{4}$	40	70
$\frac{1}{4}$ to $\frac{1}{2}$	70	110

TEMPERATURES REQUIRED IN HEAT-TREATING
VARIOUS ALUMINUM ALLOYS

ALLOY	SOAKING TEMPERATURES
A17S, 17S, Alclad 17S[a]	925– 950° F.
24S, Alclad 24S[a]	910– 930° F.
53S, 61S[a]	960– 980° F.
142[b]	940– 960° F.
195, Class I[b]	940– 970° F.
195, Class II[b]	940– 970° F.
B195[b]	940– 970° F.
355[b]	960– 980° F.
356[b]	990–1010° F.

a Hardened by heat treat, or cold work, or both.
b Hardened by heat treat alone.

Further tables, showing times and temperatures required for the heat treatment of other metals, will be found in the Appendix.

Annealing

Annealing is a heating process designed to soften, rather than harden, metals. It refines the granular structure of a metal and relieves the internal strain caused by full heat treatments or work-hardening.

Complete annealing consists of heating the metal at a required temperature until the grain is refined, and then cooling it slowly. Aluminum alloys are usually heated to temperatures of between 650° and 800° F. Steels are heated above their critical range, which is roughly as follows:

STEEL CONTENT	TEMPERATURE	RANGE
Gamma Iron	1652° F.	Upper
Beta Iron	1400° F.	Second
Alpha Iron [1]	1274° F.	Lower

Partial annealing for removal of work-hardening may be performed on all non-heat-treatable alloys, or on strong alloys during forming operations on material in the fully heat-treated condition. This process applies chiefly to aluminum alloys. The required heat is usually between 650° and 750° F.

Aluminum and Its Alloys

As an element, aluminum was first isolated in the year 1825. The dictator Napoleon heard of this metal in 1845 and decided it would make him a good suit of armor. But he found that it was more precious than gold, and he could not possibly obtain sufficient quantities for his battle regalia.

Therefore, although approximately 8 per cent of the earth's surface is aluminum, this now vital metal remained just another laboratory oddity until 1886, when a young American named Charles Martin Hall developed the modern process of extracting aluminum from bauxite ore. Curiously enough, two Europeans—Paul Heroult, a Frenchman, and Robert Bunsen, a German—stumbled on similar methods of producing aluminum at almost the same time.

While aluminum can be found in every corner of the earth, the metal is usually extracted from bauxite ore because bauxite contains

[1] Iron with low carbon content.

the greatest "pay load." The bauxite is powdered and mixed into a hot caustic soda solution. This dissolves the aluminum oxide out of the ore, along with numerous impurities. Impurities not dissolved by the caustic solution are removed in large filter presses, and the filtrate is pumped into precipitating tanks. Aluminum hydroxide is removed from the precipitating tanks, washed, and heated white-hot to dry. This procedure removes the hydrogen and again leaves aluminum oxide, or "aluminathus," in a white powder form. An electrolytic process (the secret of Hall's success) is then followed to isolate the aluminum, which is tapped into large mixing ladles and cast into "pigs," each weighing about fifty pounds.

After this, the aluminum may be remelted to remove impurities. Then the necessary alloying elements are added, if required, and the metal is poured into ingots—ready to be molded and shaped into the raw materials (sheets, bars, and so forth) from which airplanes are made.

In its pure form, aluminum is a very soft metal of low strength and very little practical value; alloyed with other metals, it remains light yet has a strength comparable to that of steel. The most common alloying substances are copper, magnesium, silicon, chromium, zinc, iron, and manganese. Generally several of these elements are used, rather than just one.

The method of designating alloys is to assign a number to the chemical composition and then add letters to designate the different conditions in which the alloy is used. Thus 17, 24, or 53 are numbers that indicate certain alloys. Letters used are:

S—a wrought product; this includes all forms except castings, which will be explained later.

O—fully annealed, the softest condition.

H—fully work-hardened, usually accomplished by rolling or bending. The symbols $\frac{1}{4}$H, $\frac{1}{2}$H, etc., designated conditions of relative hardness obtained by limited work-hardening.

W—a condition obtained by quenching, following a heat treatment yet prior to aging which completes the hardening.

T—a fully heat-treated state, resulting from aging after quenching.

RT—fully heat-treated and then cold-rolled to obtain even greater strength.

The most generally used wrought alloys, their composition, and their tempers at the time they are delivered to an aircraft factory will be found in the following table:

ALLOY	TYPE	TEMPERS	CU.**	SI.	MG.	CR.	MN.	AL.
2S	Non-H.T.*	0, 1/4H, 1/2H, 3/4H, H	--	--	--	--	--	99.5
3S	Non-H.T.	0, 1/4H, 1/2H, 3/4H, H	--	--	--	--	1.25	Bal.
14S	Strong	T	4.4	.8	.35	--	.75	Bal.
A17S	Strong	T	2.5	--	.3	--	--	Bal.
17S	Strong	0, T, RT	4.0	--	.5	--	.5	Bal.
24S	Strong	0, T, RT	4.2	--	1.5	--	.5	Bal.
52S	Non-H.T.	0, 1/4H, 1/2H, 3/4H, H	--	--	2.5	.25	--	Bal.
53S	(see note)	0, W, T	--	.7	1.25	.25	--	Bal.

*Non-heat-treatable

**Cu., copper; Si., Silicon; Mg., Magnesium; Cr., Chromium; Mn., Manganese

NOTE: 53S is too low in alloy content for spon- taneous aging at room temperature and so will remain in the W condition and is usually purchased in this temper.

Due to an insufficient percentage of certain alloying elements, many alloys cannot be strengthened by heat treatment. They must be hardened by cold work and therefore can be obtained only in the 0, ¼H, ½H, ¾H, or H tempers. Such alloys are used for severe forming, deep drawing, and similar purposes because they are very ductile and easily formed—especially in the annealed (0) condition. However, the strongest alloys are heat treatable and are generally preferred for aircraft parts of an important structural nature. Alloy forms available and commonly used for aircraft are:

2S—rods, bars, sheet, tubing, foil, rivets, wire.
3S—rods, bars, sheet.
14S—forgings, billets.
A17S—rivets.
17S—rods, bars, sheet, tubing, rivets, wire, extrusions.
24S—rods, bars, sheet, tubing, rivets, wire, extrusions.
52S—rods, bars, sheet, tubing, wire.
53S—rods, bars, sheet, tubing, rivets, wire, extrusions.

Both 17S and 24S sheets are supplied either bare or coated with aluminum in its purest form. The latter coated type is called "alclad." The coating or layer of pure aluminum is rolled on during the proc-

Pure Aluminum ←   →Dural

FIG. 12. MAGNIFIED CROSS SECTION OF ALCLAD SHEET

ess of fabrication. Its purpose is to protect the dural interior, since pure aluminum is one of the most corrosion-resistant metals known to mankind. The surface layer may vary in thickness from 0.002 to 0.006 inch, but in aircraft work the 0.005 inch type is generally preferred. In handling alclad, the main thing to remember is to avoid scratching the metal; even comparatively slight surface scratches may expose the dural interior enough to start corrosion.

Surface Protection for Aluminum Alloys

Unfortunately, many aluminum alloys do not inherit the corrosion resistance of pure aluminum. Therefore, if they are to be used for any length of time, they must be protected.

Anodizing is probably the most popular of the protective methods. This is a comparatively simple matter of forming a protective coating of aluminum oxide (or artificial rust) on the surface of the metal. It is accomplished by placing the alloy parts in a solution of chromic acid contained in a steel tank. Then, using the tank as a cathode and the respective parts as anodes, a direct current of electricity is applied. Acid reactions to the negatively charged parts cause a grayish surface film to form on the metal, and the process is complete. The aluminum oxide coating, besides protecting the metal, acts as electrical insulation and forms an excellent base for paint. The usual procedure requires an application of 40 volts for some thirty minutes. The film is soft and jelly-like at first, but a hot water rinse will facilitate its tendency to harden.

In anodizing rivets, sulphuric acid is often used in place of chromic acid. This process is followed by a sealing treatment in a boiling potassium or sodium dichromate solution. Anodizing cannot be accomplished on any alloy containing more than 5 per cent copper, or on assemblies with metal parts not made of aluminum.

Chromodizing is sometimes used in place of anodizing. This is simply a dip in a 5 per cent chromic acid solution at 140° F. for two to five minutes. It is especially effective on non-heat-treatable alloys such as 53S, etc.

Painting is an added surface protection for aluminum alloys. Several different methods are employed. The best preventers of corrosion found so far are the primers containing zinc chromate; these are applied by spraying or dipping, and are followed by top coats of the desired colors. Zinc chromate paste is also widely used on seaplane hulls and floats; it stops leaks.

Alclad sheet metal, being protected by pure aluminum, is never anodized or chromodized; however, it may be heat-treated and painted.

Working with Aluminum and Its Alloys

All aluminum alloys are easily machinable. The only general rule is to allow slightly more clearance angles and set lathe tools at a slightly higher position than is used when machining steel.

Aluminum and many of its alloys in the soft tempers, or when annealed, can be formed by all the common shop methods—such as spinning, drawing, bending by hand, and forming under a drop hammer or hydraulic press. However, such severe operations as spinning or deep drawing may necessitate annealing between operations to relieve the strain of work-hardening.

As a rule, small parts are formed by hand hammering sheet metal over a form block made of steel, zinc, or wood. Either a fiber or rawhide hammer may be used in this operation without damaging the material. Large parts are often made on drop hammers, using dies made of numerous types of metal.

A complete treatise on the bending of light gauge metal, which is usually accomplished on a "brake" or set of "rolls," will be found in the chapter on Shop Practice.

Insofar as is practicable, aluminum alloys are formed after, rather than before, a heat treatment; this is in order to avoid warping after the quenching process. Also, in designing forming tools (blocks, dies, and so forth), an allowance must be made for "spring back" in aluminum alloys; otherwise, the angles obtained will be insufficient. For example, in using annealed material, parts must be over-formed by about 3 degrees in order to attain a specified shape.

Aluminum and aluminum alloy sheet metals are actually manufactured in conformity with the Brown and Sharpe gauge. However, neither the gauge number nor the actual thickness is usually given when referring to such metals in an aircraft factory; only the decimal of an inch indicating the thickness is commonly used. Hence, measurements run as shown in the table on page 50.

Wrought alloys, which are worked hot during fabrication, are the most commonly used metals in aircraft work. They are the sheet, bar, rod, forgings, wire, and extrusions mentioned previously. And, of these, sheet and extruded sections comprise a majority of the structural materials used in an airplane. The sheet metal is rolled to the required thickness, then stretched beyond its elastic limit to remove irregularities; this is called "stretcher-leveling." Extrusions are made by forcing semimolten metal through a steel die, as explained and shown in Figure 13.

Not as important as the wrought alloys, but nonetheless used, are alloy sand castings. The 195-T6, 220-T4, and 356-T6 combinations

Gauge Number	Commonly Termed	Actual Thickness
30	.010	.01003
26	.016	.01594
25	.018	.01790
24	.020	.02010
23	.022	.02257
22	.025	.02535
21	.028	.02846
20	.032	.03196
19	.036	.03589
18	.040	.04030
17	.045	.04526
16	.051	.05082
15	.057	.05707
14	.064	.06408
13	.072	.07196
12	.081	.08081
11	.091	.09074
9	.114	.1144
8	.128	.1285

are generally used for this work, and all are heat treatable. Die castings are rarely used for structural parts, but may be found in nonstressed parts; aluminum alloys 13, 43, and 85 are suitable for this work—the 43 alloy being preferred when a casting is to be welded.

After being welded, aluminum alloy parts are usually "pickled." This process consists of dipping a part in a 5 or 10 per cent solution of sulphuric acid at a temperature of about 145° F. for a period of

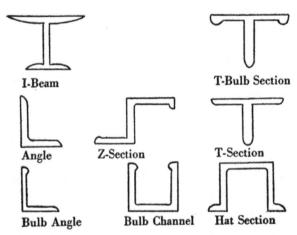

FIG. 13. EXTRUDED SECTIONS OF ALUMINUM, FORMED BY
FORCING SEMIMOLTEN METAL THROUGH A STEEL DIE

from five to fifteen minutes. Thus, rust and scales are eliminated and corrosion is prevented.

Aluminum rivets, their composition, and types will be discussed in Chapter 7.

Airplane Steels

Steels used in the aircraft industry have a tensile strength of from 55,000 pounds per square inch to about 250,000 pounds per square inch. They are listed in accordance with a system set up by the Society of Automotive Engineers (S.A.E.) for the sake of brevity.

The first, or basic, numeral in this system indicates the type of steel. Hence, "1" is a carbon steel; "2" is a nickel steel; "3" is a nickel-chromium steel.

In designating simple alloy steels, the second digit usually shows the approximate percentage of the predominant alloying element, and the last two or three numbers indicate the average carbon content in terms of hundredths of 1 per cent. For example, "2340" indicates a nickel steel of about 3 per cent nickel (3.25 to 3.75), and 0.40 per cent carbon (0.35 to 0.45).

To avoid confusion, it has in several instances been found necessary to depart from this system of identifying the approximate alloy composition of a steel by varying the second and third digits of a number—for example, steel numbers selected for several of the corrosion and heat-resisting alloys. However, the basic S.A.E. system remains as follows: [2]

Type of Steel	Numerals and Digits
Carbon steels	1xxx
Plain carbon	10xx
Free cutting (screw stock)	11xx
Manganese steels	13xx
Nickel Steels	2xxx
3.50 per cent nickel	23xx
5.00 per cent nickel	25xx
Nickel-chromium steels	3xxx
$\frac{1}{2.5}$ per cent nickel, 0.60 per cent chromium	31xx
1.75 per cent nickel, 1.00 per cent chromium	32xx
3.50 per cent nickel, 1.50 per cent chromium	33xx
Corrosion and heat-resisting steels	30xxx
Molybdenum steels	4xxx
Carbon molybdenum	40xx
Chromium molybdenum	41xx
Chromium-nickel molybdenum	43xx
Nickel molybdenum, 1.75 per cent nickel	46xx
Nickel molybdenum, 3.50 per cent nickel	48xx
Chromium steels	5xxx
Low chromium	51xx

[2] Courtesy of Society of Automotive Engineers.

Medium chromium 52xxx
Corrosion and heat resisting 51xxx

Chromium-vanadium steels 6xxx
1 per cent chromium 61xx

Silicon-manganese steels 9xxx
2 per cent silicon 92xx

As everyone knows, the basic element in steel is iron. Iron is converted into steel by three methods—the Bessemer open-hearth process, the crucible process, and the electric process. Each of these processes results in wrought steel; cast steel is made from wrought-steel scrap by melting in a furnace and casting in sand molds. The difference between steel and iron is the fact that the latter usually contains more than 1.7 per cent carbon. Therefore, the primary purpose of a steel-producing process is to reduce the carbon content of iron. However, the difference in physical properties is a far more complicated matter.

Iron has less than half the tensile strength of steel on a basis of average comparisons; its corrosion resistance and hardness are comparatively negligible, while steel is the hardest and one of the best self-protected metals in existence.

In the aircraft industry, the most commonly used steels are S.A.E. 1025, 2330, and X4130. The latter is chrome-molybdenum steel containing about 1 per cent chromium and 0.25 to 0.35 per cent carbon; it is usually called "Chrome-Moly."

Chrome-molybdenum is the most popular of all aircraft steels, and is used in a great number of structural parts. S.A.E. 1025, a mild carbon steel, is popular in engine mounts because of its ability to resist vibrations. S.A.E. 2330, sometimes called "3½ per cent nickel," is the standard Army and Navy metal for nuts, bolts, high-strength fittings, and shafts.

Sometimes, when great resistance to corrosion is essential as well as strength, "stainless steels" are used. These are steels containing chromium, or both chromium and nickel; they come in three classes and have the following properties:

GROUP	ANALYSIS	MAGNETIC	HEAT TREATMENT HARDEN ABILITY
A	% Cr. -(17 x % C) is under 12.5%	yes	Same as any ordinary steel
B	% Cr. -(17 x % C) is more than 12.5	yes	Will not respond
C	Over 7% Ni. and %Cr.+ % Ni. = over 24%	No	Will not respond

Technically speaking, chrome-molybdenum is a stainless steel, but it is rarely referred to as such.

The group C steels shown in the table above are frequently used in aircraft work, and can be hardened only by cold work. Titanium, columbium, or molybdenum should be added to these steels before they are welded or operated at temperatures of more than 1000° F. This prevents intergranular corrosion. Selenium or zirconium sulphides make steels in this group easier to machine.

The group B stainless steels are rarely used in aircraft work.

Steel in the sheet form is used almost exclusively for fittings. Since this type of work necessitates sharp bends and welding, S.A.E. 1025 and X4130 are preferred. However, if considerable strength is required, S.A.E. 6150 (chrome-vanadium steel) may be used. When using the latter metal, welding must be performed prior to the heat treatment.

Bar steels used in aircraft construction are usually plain carbon steels such as S.A.E. 1015, 1020, 1035, and 1045. These are for machined parts and forgings.

Steel #1015 is popular in case-hardened parts. Case-hardening is a carburizing process followed by a heat treatment. Carburizing is a method of adding carbon to steel at high temperatures; its purpose is to harden the surface of the metal.

"Inconel" is a nickel-chromium steel widely used for the manufacture of exhaust stacks because of its corrosion resistance. Most forgings are S.A.E. 4130 or 4140 type steels.

"Alloy," or stainless steels, are used largely for bolts, pins, clevises, and other highly stressed parts. Here a tensile strength of more than 100,000 pounds per square inch is required; it is generally developed through heat treatments.

The three types of steel wire used in the aircraft industry may be classified as hard, stranded, and tie-rods. Hard wire is a single strand of high tensile strength steel (S.A.E. 1050 to 1095). Stranded wire comprises a number of small strands twined together, like cable. Tie-rods are single strands with threaded ends; they come with cross sections that are round, square, or streamlined.

Stranded wire may be further termed "nonflexible," "flexible," and "extra flexible." The nonflexible type has nineteen strands and is used only for bracing. The flexible and extra flexible types vary in size, but are generally used on pulleys.

Since all carbon steels—regardless of form—have the same general appearance, a code of painted stripes is used to designate the composition of each rod, sheet, bar, or tube. This is to avoid confusion.

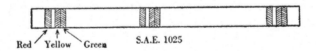

Red / Yellow ↑ \ Green   S.A.E. 1025

FIG. 14. EXAMPLE OF STEEL MARKING SYSTEM

Three sets of stripes are painted on each piece of material—one set at each end, and another in the middle. A set usually comprises one stripe five inches wide and another stripe two inches wide, separated by a space of about one inch; the first stripe represents the first part of the S.A.E. number, and the second stripe represents the remaining two digits. If either stripe is composed of two colors, each color occupies half of the stripe. The "stripe code" is shown in the following color-marking table:

COLOR MARKING OF CARBON STEEL ALLOYS

Color	First part of steel number	Color	Last two digits of steel numbers
Red	10	Red and Black	00
Red and White	11	Red	10
Red and Yellow	13	Red and Green	12
Yellow	23	Red and White	15
Yellow and Green	25	Yellow	20
Green	31	Yellow and White	25
Blue	32	Black	30
Brown	33	Black and White	35
Black	34	Green	40
Black and White	41	Green and White	45
Red and Black	46	Black and Green	46
Khaki	51	Blue	50
Red and Blue	53	Brown	60
White	61	Brown and White	65
Red and Brown	72	Khaki	95

An orange stripe indicates annealed stock.
A gray stripe indicates heat treated stock.

Stainless steels are usually marked with a rubber stamp so as to show an American Iron and Steel Institute (A.I.S.I.) formula number and a temper symbol. For example:

(1) 302–1A means alloy 302, annealed.
(2) 304–½H means alloy 304, half hardened.
(3) 410–1H means alloy 410, fully hardened.
(4) Inconel–1A means inconel in the annealed state.
(5) Inconel–1H means inconel fully hardened.

The A.I.S.I. alloys used in the aircraft industry are numbered 302, 303, 304, 321, 347, and 410. They correspond roughly with the S.A.E. chrome-nickel steels.

Special Steel Processes

Like aluminum, steel can be either heat-treated or annealed. The only difference in processes here is a matter of time and temperature, the variations of which will be found in the Appendix.

Sometimes the steel-annealing process is called "normalizing." It should not be confused with the "neutralizing" process, which comprises a lime bath to remove exterior impurities from the metal.

"Passivating" stainless steel is similar to anodizing aluminum. The purpose of the process is to form an oxide coating on the metal. It is accomplished in a 15 to 20 per cent nitric acid bath at 150° F. in a period of about twenty minutes; it is followed by a thorough rinse in running water.

"Pickling" steel is usually preceded by a lye bath to remove grease from the metal. Its purpose is to remove the rust and scale resulting from welding operations, and it consists of a five to fifteen minute bath in a 5 to 10 per cent solution of sulphuric acid at a temperature of about 145° F.

"Sand blasting" is a method of scouring steel with compressed air and a very fine grade of sand. It cleans and roughens the surface of the metal, leaving a good surface for plating or painting.

Most popular of modern methods to remove grease from metals is the trichlorethlene vapor "degreaser." Steam coils in the bottom

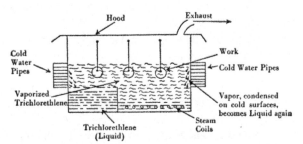

FIG. 15. VAPOR DEGREASER

of the degreaser (see Figure 15) vaporize the trichlorethlene. The vapor cleans the metal, then comes in contact with cold water pipes and becomes a liquid again.

Cadmium plating is one of the best methods of protecting ordinary steels from corrosion. Parts that have been cadmium plated will stand a 250-hour salt-spray test without signs of deteriorating. This process will be described in detail later.

Stainless steels get their mirror-like aspect by a special pickling bath of about 10 per cent nitric acid and 3 per cent hydrochloric acid at 160° F. This is followed by a hot water rinse, and the previously described passivation treatment.

Magnesium and Its Alloys

Discovered as an element in 1830, magnesium was not commercialized until about 1900. Then its chief value was as an ingredient for fireworks, photographic flash powder, explosives, and similar products. It is still used for some of these purposes, although recent experiments have proved it to have great potentialities for aircraft work.

Magnesium is strong, yet it weighs only a little more than half as much as aluminum. However, because of the fact that it is not naturally fire and corrosion resistant, its alloys are not often used for structural parts.

At present magnesium alloys are available in the form of sheets, extrusions, rods in standard gauges, castings, and forgings. These are used to make crank cases, instrument housings, landing-gear tail wheels, and so forth.

An electrolytic process developed in Germany made the commercial production of magnesium possible; it is not unlike the process used in obtaining aluminum.

The two strongest and most widely used magnesium alloys are the "ternary" and "quaternary" types. The latter comprises aluminum, zinc, and manganese alloys.

As a rule, magnesium alloys are fabricated by machining, cutting, forming, welding, or riveting. Molten magnesium has a tendency to burn, while cold-forming sometimes causes the metal to crack.

Insulation is necessary when magnesium alloys are used to make parts containing other metals. Cellophane and zinc chromate, or aluminum foil where possible, serve this purpose—which is a precautionary measure against static electricity, the electrolytic action of which would quickly corrode the magnesium involved.

Magnesium rivets are used infrequently in aircraft work; their low shear strength makes them impractical for most structural parts. A magnesium alloy containing 4 or 5 per cent aluminum can be torch welded without difficulty.

Since the Dow Chemical Company is the foremost producer of magnesium alloys at present, Dow symbols are usually accepted as a standard when working with these metals. Less frequently used are American Magnesium (AM) symbols. The accompanying table shows the more familiar symbols (of both types) and points out the composition of the alloys they represent.

SYMBOLS AND COMPOSITION OF MAGNESIUM ALLOYS

Dow Symbols	A.M. Symbols	Composition[a]					
		Al.	Mn.	Cd.	Zn.	Cu.	Si.
A	AM–241	8.0	0.15	...	...	...	...
B	AM–246	12.0	0.10	...	...	...	...
F	AM–53S	4.0	0.20	...	...	...	...
G	AM–240	10.0	0.10	...	...	...	...
H	AM–265	6.0	0.15	...	3.0	...	...
J	AM–57S	6.9	0.15	...	0.7	...	...
K	AM–230	10.0	0.10	...	...	...	0.75
M	AM–3S	...	1.50	...	...	...	...
M	AM–405	...	1.50	...	...	...	...
..	(Cast)	...	1.50	...	...	...	...
O	AM–58S	8.5	0.15	...	0.5	...	...
E	....	6.0	0.30	...	...	...	...
L	....	2.5	0.20	...	...	...	...
P	....	10.0	0.10	...	2.0	...	...
T	....	2.0	0.20	2.0	...	4.0	...
X	....	3.0	0.20	...	3.0	...	...
EX	....	6.5	0.20	...	...	...	0.20
R	....	9.0	0.13	...	0.6	...	...

a Figures denote percentages.
Al.—aluminum.   Zn.—zinc.
Mn.—manganese.   Cu.—copper.
Cd.—cadmium.   Si.—silicon.

At present there are two methods of protecting magnesium alloys against salt water corrosion. They are:

(1) *Chrome-pickle treatment*—a bath lasting from one to three minutes in a solution of sodium dichromate, concentrated nitric acid, and water. This solution is kept in an aluminum tank, and after the bath the part is rinsed in cold water, then hot water. The consequent protective film that has been formed is soft at first, but hardens as it dries to a thickness of about 0.001 to 0.002 inch.

(2) *Dow treatment No. 7*—a five-minute dip in a 15 per cent solution of hydrofluoric acid at room temperature, or a forty-five-minute boiling treatment in a 10 per cent solution of sodium dichromate. This treatment will not affect close dimensions, and can be used on magnesium parts after they are machined. All surfaces, even deep holes, generally react the same to this treatment. However, it is not very satisfactory for sheet products.

Beryllium

The history of beryllium to date has been chiefly that of a minor alloy. It has not yet found a fitting occupation in the American aircraft industry. However, Germany and Japan have made considerable progress in the use of this remarkable metal—and our scientists are at present anxiously striving to make up for lost time.

About 30 per cent lighter than aluminum, beryllium has a melting point nearly double that of either magnesium or aluminum. It is highly elastic, and is said to present effective natural resistance to corrosion.

Beryl ore, from which beryllium is extracted, is imported to a great extent from Brazil and Argentina. However, it has recently been located in considerable quantities in both the United States and Canada. And scientists claim that each cubic mile of the earth's surface contains some 144,000 tons of this metal.

In comparatively small quantities, beryllium is now available in the sheet and bar forms, alloyed with aluminum. Also, it is said to have sufficient workability to be used for aircraft forgings.

Springs made from beryllium-aluminum alloys will contract and expand almost twice as many times as springs made of steel. And copper, with 2 per cent beryllium as an alloy, becomes almost four times as strong as aluminum; but unfortunately the latter combina- tion is too heavy for general use in aircraft work.

The latest developments in the use of beryllium are now a mili- tary secret, but ambitious aircraft workers, who desire a place of importance in the industry of the future, will do well to keep this metal in mind.

Alloying Elements

While aluminum, steel, magnesium, and beryllium at present oc-. cupy the metallurgical spotlight for the aircraft industry, numerous alloying elements are also of vital importance and some knowledge of their properties is essential. These can be listed as follows:

Carbon—generally the most important element in steel, despite the fact that all steel-producing processes are designed to decrease the percentage of carbon in iron. A small percentage of carbon makes, steel hard and strong; too much carbon causes excessive brittleness.

Manganese—a "deoxidizing" agent, which removes the "red short-. ness" or hot brittleness caused by the presence of sulphur in a metal. The percentage of manganese should be six times that of sulphur. Steels with more than 12 per cent manganese become nonmagnetic after quenching at high temperatures; they are also very hard and durable. The average percentage of manganese in a metal is 1 or 2 per cent.

Phosphorus—usually considered an impurity in steel; one of the purposes of the open-hearth process is to reduce it to less than 0.05 per cent. A high phosphorus content increases the fluidity of molten metal, but causes the finished product to be too brittle. Copper and phosphorus together increase the corrosion resistance of steel.

Sulphur—also generally considered an impurity. The open-hearth process for steel reduces it to 0.05 per cent, but 0.25 per cent will give the metal better machinability.

Silicon—found in iron ore. In amounts under 0.75 per cent it is considered an impurity, but in amounts of 0.75 to 2.5 per cent it increases the metal's strength. More than 2.5 per cent of silicon enhances corrosion resistance, but makes metals too brittle for aircraft work. Generally chromium and silicon are combined to make steel corrosion and heat resistant without losing the metal's elasticity.

Copper—found in small percentages in all steel, though by itself it is not practical for aircraft work. It increases the life of metals generally, and is the main element in the bronzes and brasses which are so frequently used in bolts, turnbuckles, oil strainers, etc. The accompanying table shows the composition of the principal brasses and bronzes and their uses.

COMPOSITION AND USES OF PRINCIPAL BRASSES AND BRONZES

MATERIAL	COMPOSITION				USES
	Copper	Tin	Lead	Iron	
Naval Brass or Tobin Bronze	60%	0.50 to 1.50	0.30	0.10	Bolts, Turnbuckles, Machine Products
Brass Sheet	64–67%	...	0.30	0.05	Oil Strainers
Manganese Bronze	53–62%	Zinc 38–47	0.15	...	Sand Castings
Leaded Gun Metal	86–89%	Tin 9–11	1.00– 2.50	Phos. 0.25	Bushings
Phosphor Bronze Wire	93–95%	4–6 ª	0.10	0.03– 0.40	Flat or Wire Springs

ª Also Zinc, 0.20%.

Nickel—found in low quantities, like copper, it increases the life of metals by increasing their atmospheric corrosion resistance. In quantities of 1 to 5 per cent, it dissolves ferrite and strengthens steel by refining its grain. As has been stated previously, stainless steels usually contain a large percentage of nickel.

Chromium—another important element in stainless steels. The three general classes of stainless steels are:

(1) Austentic—with over 7 per cent nickel and 17 per cent chromium.

(2) Ferritic—with over 15 per cent chromium and less than 13 per cent carbon.

(3) Martensitic—with less than 15 per cent chromium and over 10 per cent carbon.

High percentages of chromium increase the corrosion and heat resistance of metals.

Molybdenum—increases the hardness and strength of steels, especially at high temperatures, and reduces brittleness. It is frequently used in combinations of chromium, nickel, and vanadium.

Tungsten—is similar to molybdenum in its effect on iron and steel, but is required in greater quantities. This alloy is used largely in steels that are to be used for high-speed tools, a typical formula for which is 8 per cent tungsten, 4 per cent chromium, and 1.25 per cent vanadium.

Vanadium—used in small percentages with other alloys to refine the grain and thus strengthen and toughen metals. It is a good deoxidizer, but too expensive for general use. It is found generally in high-speed steels.

Cobalt—similar to nickel, but too expensive for general use. It is used mainly in magnets and super high-speed steels in quantities of about 4 per cent.

Titanium and columbium—used to prevent air hardening in intermediate steels containing chromium. These alloys have a marked attraction for carbon, which results in various carbides.

Lead—improves machinability and refines the grain of metals, but impairs the hot workability of steel.

Nitrogen—a gas which promotes ductility and grain refinement in high chromium steels.

Metalizing or Metal Spraying

Metalizing is a process whereby a part made of one metal can be protected by a coating of another metal. It is similar to the familiar paint-spraying operation.

Copper, zinc, tin, steel, aluminum, and stainless steel are the metals generally used for the spraying, and the following equipment is required:

(1) Wire of the preferred metal.
(2) Oxygen and acetylene.
(3) Portable spray gun.
(4) Compressed air.

The compressed air is usually provided by a turbine and controls the speed of the operation.

The surface of the metal to be sprayed must be cleaned thoroughly. Then the wire is melted by the combined oxygen and acetylene flame. Compressed air atomizes the molten metal and blows it in the desired direction. The coating may be built up to any desired thickness.

Besides protecting metals, this process may be used to build up worn parts or to fill unnecessary holes.

Cadmium Plating

Cadmium plating is the cheapest, yet most efficient, method of protecting steel, bronze, and brass parts used in making airplanes. Cadmium-plated parts are especially favored in seaplanes because of their great resistance to salt-water corrosion.

Cadmium is found in the form of cadmium sulphide—a metal somewhat harder than tin, yet malleable, ductile, and readily volatile. It was first discovered during a zinc extraction process. It has a tin-white color, a fibrous structure, and takes a high polish.

Effective cadmium plating must be smooth and uniform, and the material that is to be plated should therefore be clean and grease-

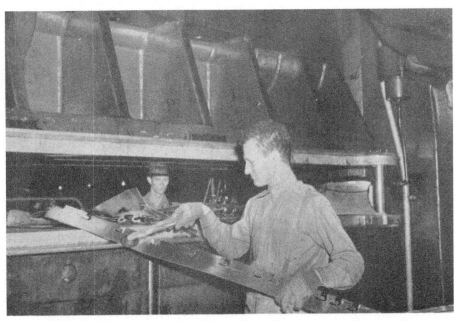

Above. The sheet of aluminum alloy metal that is being removed has just been formed over a steel die under the big hydraulic press in the background. (*Consolidated Aircraft Corp. Photo*)

Below. An example of metal forming. (*Lockheed Aircraft Corp. Photo*)

Above. Workmen are installing a transparent plexiglass nose in a Flying Fortress bomber. (*Boeing Aircraft Co. Photo*)

Below. These girls are lacing fabric on the center section framework for a trailing edge. Note heavy "thread" used. (*Consolidated Aircraft Corp. Photo*)

free. Parts that are cadmium plated include screws, nuts, bolts, steel springs, brass bushings. Steel springs require a special baking treatment at 400° F. for three to four hours after plating. This relieves the embrittlement of the steel from the pickling process which precedes the plating. When copper alloys come in contact with iron or steel, cadmium plating will prevent electrolysis. Paint adheres poorly to cadmium-plated surfaces unless the surfaces are first etched by a bath in a 5 per cent solution of chromic acid.

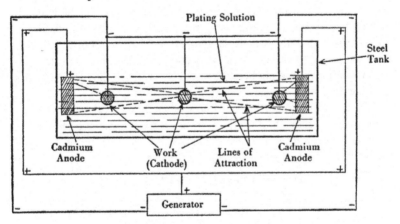

FIG. 16. CADMIUM PLATING TANK

The two types of cadmium plating are "still plating" and "barrel plating." The first type is accomplished in a stationary steel tank and is most effective on large parts. The second type is accomplished in a revolving barrel and is most effective on small parts such as nuts or bolts.

Still-plating equipment includes:

(1) Generator and motor set, bus bars, rheostat.
(2) Parts baskets.
(3) Tanks for pre-cleaning.
(4) Tanks for rinsing.
(5) Wooden tanks for acid pickling and rinsing.
(6) Steel tank for plating.

(7) Steel tank for plating rinse.

(8) Hot-air or sawdust drying equipment.

Barrel-plating equipment is the same as still-plating equipment, except for the fact that a steel barrel is used for plating rather than a steel tank.

A standard six-volt generator suffices for still plating, but barrel-plating requirements may vary.

As previously explained, metals must be cleaned and degreased before plating. Methods of accomplishing this may include hand-wiping with solvents or thinners, sand blasting, tumbling or burnishing, steam vapor degreasing, hot water soaking, soaking in alkaline solutions, acid pickling. Most important of these methods in cadmium plating is the acid-pickling process, which removes rust scales and welding flux.

The actual plating solution comprises cadmium oxide, sodium cyanide, caustic soda, and water. The accompanying table shows the required percentages of these chemicals and the conditions required for each of the two types of cadmium plating.

CADMIUM-PLATING REQUIREMENTS

MATERIAL AND CONDITION	STILL PLATING	BARREL PLATING
Cadmium Oxide	3 oz. per gal.	3–4 oz. per gal.
Sodium Cyanide	13 oz. per gal.	13–15 oz. per gal.
Caustic Soda	None—formed by other chemicals	None—formed by other chemicals
Brightener	Used as required	Used as required
Temperature	70–100° F.	70–100° F.
Current (Cathode) ..	10–15 amps. sq. ft.	2–10 amps. sq. ft.
Voltage	2–2½ volts	6–12 volts
Anodes	Pure cadmium, with or without steel anodes	Pure cadmium, or proprietary brands like "Cad-a-loy" anodes containing 0.5% mercury
Sodium Cyanide (free)	9.5–10 oz. per gal.	9.5–10 oz. gal.

Brighteners used in cadmium plating include glue, casein, sulpho-nated castor oil. They are used only when metallic whiteness is essential.

The theory of cadmium plating is the same as that of any electroplating process. It consists of transferring a material from one surface to another by means of a positive current of electricity which can be attracted by a negative (or cathode) pole.

Minimum thickness for cadmium plate is 0.0005 inch, except where threads (as on a machine screw) are concerned. In the latter instance, a thickness of 0.0002 inch will suffice. Time required for the 0.0005-inch thickness depends on the number of amperes employed, roughly as follows:

AMPERES PER SQ. FT.	TIME (MINUTES)
17.70	10
8.85	20
5.95	30
4.46	40

Plastics

Nonstructural plastic parts—such as bakelite control knobs, plexiglass windshields, or nylon lining—have been used in the manufacture of airplanes for several years. However, the use of plywood and plastics for the fabrication of fuselages and wings is a comparatively recent development which is destined to become of increasing importance in the very near future.

Shellac was probably the first modern plastic; it was developed in the middle of the nineteenth century and has been popular ever since. But plastics as a group did not achieve much recognition until the year 1922—thirteen years after the discovery of "bakelite," a phenol-formaldehyde composition originated by a Dr. Baekeland. In 1922, the manufacture of plastics became another American Big Business—a status which is retained on an ever increasing scale today.

Plastics can be made from almost anything—farm products, carbolic acid, petroleum products, coal, ammonia, wood, fabric, and so forth. But still they can be classified in four main groups—phenolic resins, urea plastics, cellulose acetates, and vinyls.

Phenolic resins, which include the previously mentioned bakelite, are most common. The so-called laminated plastics belong to this group; they are fabricated on layers of cloth or papers which are pressed and baked between hot plates. Besides being relatively cheap, phenolic resins are easy to mold and highly resistant to chemicals and heat.

Urea plastics are also easy to mold; they come in numerous colors and have a fine luster if the molds have been properly polished. They have an exceedingly hard surface, especially after the addition of cellulose, and will withstand temperatures of as much as 170° F.

Cellulose acetates are softer than most plastics, but also less inflammable. They may be molded in much the same manner as metal extrusions, in a semifluid condition and under pressure. Their colors are often varied and unusual. They withstand shock, but have little resistance to water.

Vinyls vary in physical properties. On the whole, however, they are easily molded, have good machinability, and are adhesive as well as elastic. Hence, they are widely used in safety glass.

Generally speaking, the ingredients used in making a plastic do not undergo a simple chemical change; they "polymerize" (that is, they combine by enlargement of the molecular structure without a change in chemical composition). A catalyst is necessary to attain this reaction, and one of the two following physical settings is the result:

        (1) Thermosetting.
        (2) Thermoplastic.

Thermosetting plastic materials are manufactured as granular materials, and are shaped or molded under heat or pressure. Heat and pressure cause them to become infusible, and they are somewhat expensive to mold. They cannot be resoftened by heat or remolded. Inert fillers—such as fuller's earth or asbestos—are added to the granular resin before it is cured. Uncured granular resins may be applied to wood or laminated wood.

Thermoplastic materials (which include the cellulose acetate group) do not react to heat and may be reformed or remolded. They are not expensive to cast, and may be used as a bonding layer in laminated wood or glass. Airplane dopes (cellulose nitrates and acetates) are thermoplastics.

The more familiar plastic trade names, grouped according to their physical settings, are:

THERMOSETTINGS	THERMOPLASTICS
Bakelite	Lumerith
Catalin	Fibestos
Durez	Plastacele
Fiberlon	Protectoid
Phenalin	Tenite
Textolite	Nixonite
Durite	Celluloid
Indur	Fiberloid
Haveg	Pyralin
Resinex	Nixonoid
Joanite	Plexiglass
Marflotte	Lucite
Phenolin	Diakon
Beetle	Leukon
Plaskon	Perspex
Unyte	Acetate
Makalot	Plastacele

Plexiglass is probably the most important plastic in the aircraft industry at the present time. It is used for windshields and the all-important machine gun "blisters" in military planes. The physical properties of plexiglass vary in accordance with the temperature. At a "normal" temperature of 25° or 30° C., it transmits light at a rate of about 92 per cent without the scattering effect of glass. Its specific gravity is 1.18 to 1.19, and, while it is not especially hard, it has great tensile, flexural, and compressive strength—enough to deflect a bullet that does not hit it squarely. The following data are frequently used in working with plexiglass:

		WEIGHT IN LBS.	
THICKNESS	TOLERANCE	Per Sq. In.	Per Sq. Ft.
0.060	0.006	.00260	.375
.070	.008	.00303	.437
.083	.008	.00361	.520
.095	.010	.00417	.600
.120	.010	.00510	.735
.140	.010	.00608	.875
.158	.010	.00687	.990
.195	.012	.00868	1.250
.220	.015	.00951	1.370
0.240	0.015	.01042	1.500

Plywood is generally considered a plastic, but it is really a combination of wood and plastics—that is, veneer sheets cemented together by plastics under heat or pressure. Mahogany plywood compares favorably with aluminum in equal strength-weight ratios, but requires a much thicker cross section.

The so-called plastic airplanes (made of plywood) are literally cooked in the primary-assembly operation. There are several patented methods of doing this. Generally, the fuselage and wing are formed separately over wooden molds; then they are placed in an airtight chamber and subjected to steam pressure. The result is unusually strong parts, requiring but little exterior bracing. No mechanical fastenings are required before the airplane reaches the final assembly stage. The formed sections will not be affected by heat, cold, dampness, corrosion, salt water, or metallic fatigue.

Dopes and Fabrics

Contrary to popular beliefs, doped fabrics are by no means obsolete in the business of building airplanes. Although these materials are no longer used throughout the airplane as skin, no altogether suitable substitute for covering control surfaces, trailing edges, and similar parts has yet been found.

The fabric most generally used is grade *A* cotton, which weighs approximately two ounces per square yard. As explained previously, the dope used to treat the fabric may be either cellulose nitrate or cellulose acetate (commonly known as lacquer). Each of these dopes may be clear, semipigmented, or fully pigmented; their purpose is to make fabric air- and watertight, and sometimes to provide color.

Acetate dopes are the least inflammable, but nitrate dopes are affected less by moisture. Generally, the nitrate type is used externally while the acetate type is used internally. As for colors, yellow is generally considered best because it presents the most resistance to sunlight.

Before being used, the fabric must be bleached in an acid solution and rinsed in water. Then it is stretched evenly over the frame—not tight enough to cause the frame to buckle. The fabric is held in place by laces, which are reinforced with tape. Sharp edges on the framework should be padded before the cloth is applied, and necessary holes in the cloth should be strongly reinforced.

Normally, six coats of dope are required. The first coat may actually make the cloth sag. Each coat should be given about an hour to dry, even though it may appear to dry instantly.

Neoprene and Thiokol

Most people believe Uncle Sam never took much interest in artificial rubber prior to Pearl Harbor, but actually artificial rubber products have been used in the aircraft industry for several years—and in some respects they are better than the real thing. Neoprene and thiokol are examples of this.

There are several types of thiokol on the market at present. One type is strong enough to be used in tires (an unusual quality in artificial rubbers), but the type best known in aircraft work is that used in the self-sealing fuel lines and cells of military planes. Besides being resistant to high-test gasoline, it has a tendency to expand when punctured (by a bullet or metal fragment), thus preventing disastrous leaks.

Neoprene is probably the most widely used of the synthetic rubbers. It is also used in fuel cells and fuel lines, because of its high resistance to the aromatic fuels. It is as strong as natural rubber in tensile strength, but is not altogether suitable for tires because it lacks abrasion resistance. It is a good heat insulator and will not deteriorate in sunlight like natural rubber.

P.A.W. tape, made from neoprene, is used to seal riveted joints, pontoons, hulls, and watertight compartments in seaplanes or flying boats. It may also be used in pressure cabins, designed for high altitude flying.

6

SHOP PRACTICE

Before a workman can undertake even the simplest job in any factory, he must first be able to follow instructions. This is not just a matter of listening to what the lead-man says and then acting accordingly; for the lead-man and his superiors are paid to supervise—not to instruct.

It is a matter of being able to comprehend engineering data, no matter how it is transmitted.

When lofting methods apply, this may be comparatively simple. It takes no imagination whatsoever to pick up a template, or any other life-sized pattern, and form a part which will be satisfactory. But working from drawings or sketches is an altogether different proposition.

Most aircraft drawings are reproduced in the form of blueprints. Making blueprints is a photographic process of transferring black lines on a white background into white lines on a blue background. This process is used in preference to other methods of reproduction mainly because it is the least expensive.

Sometimes, however, sketches with a white background may be used in order to hurry up a job, since the production of blueprints may require considerable time.

The chief difference between a finished blueprint drawing and a sketch is that the latter is likely to be made with greater haste and less regard for details. And a knowledge of drafting is necessary in order to understand either form.

73

Drafting

Drafting is the technique of making a picture that will show the size, shape, and composition of an object. This is accomplished by means of figures, printed instructions, and lines.

Figures are used to show dimensions, and are especially important in drawings that are not the exact size of the object they represent.

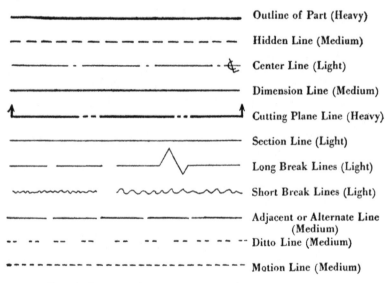

Outline of Part (Heavy)

Hidden Line (Medium)

Center Line (Light)

Dimension Line (Medium)

Cutting Plane Line (Heavy)

Section Line (Light)

Long Break Lines (Light)

Short Break Lines (Light)

Adjacent or Alternate Line (Medium)

Ditto Line (Medium)

Motion Line (Medium)

FIG. 17. AMERICAN STANDARDS ASSOCIATION "LINE ALPHABET"

Printed instructions are usually abbreviations which indicate the material from which the object is to be made. For example, S.A.E. numbers would most likely be used to show the metal required in a standard steel part.

Although frequently subject to variations, lines have been standardized by the American Standards Association into an "alphabet" which is listed in Figure 17 and shown in practical use in Figure 18.

The two general types of drawings used to convey engineering data are the "pictorial" and "orthographic" types, the latter being most common.

A pictorial drawing is any illustration which shows three sides of an object in a single view. A "true" pictorial drawing with exact dimensions and a fitting perspective is difficult to make, even for a highly skilled artist. Hence, pictorial drawings which simulate the perspective are frequently used in aircraft work. These are called *projections,* and

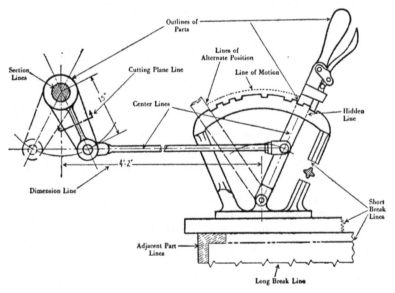

FIG. 18. THE ALPHABET OF LINES IN PRACTICAL USE

their purpose is to give the workman an over-all "plan" view of the object to be constructed.

Oblique and isometric projections are easiest to make, and therefore are most often used. An isometric projection is a drawing with three axes, each at an angle of 120°, with all measurements along or parallel to these axes. An oblique projection also has three axes, two of them at right (90°) angles from one another, with parallel and oblique lines, which may appear somewhat distorted.

The oblique illustration in Figure 19B is really a "cabinet" projection, because the oblique lines *A* and *B* have been shortened in order to present a true perspective. If lines *A* and *B* were made as long as

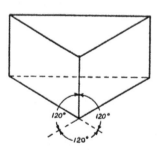

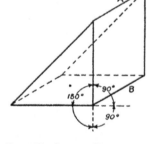

FIG. 19A. ISOMETRIC PROJECTION   FIG. 19B. OBLIQUE PROJECTION

the equivalent lines in the isometric projection, we would have a true oblique projection—but it would appear distorted. Both of the projections shown here are of a triangular block; note the differences in size.

The orthographic type of drawing presents a single view of an object, and an orthographic *projection* consists of two or more such drawings—each showing a different side of the same object. For example, the drawing of the PB2Y flying boat in Chapter 3 is a typical three-view orthographic projection.

The maximum number of views in a single orthographic projection are six. Using an ordinary square box as an example, these views would be laid out as in Figure 20A, with the pictorial drawing represented by Figure 20B.

The number of views used in an orthographic projection depend on the number of details required by the workman in order to construct a part. Plans for a square box, such as the one illustrated, would ordinarily require only a top view and a front view; the remaining views could be omitted because they would simply be duplications.

Sometimes, when the exact composition of a part cannot be shown by abbreviations or printed instructions on the drawing proper, a

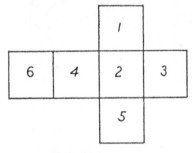

1—Top view
2—Front view
3—Right (or Profile) view

4—Left view
5—Bottom view
6—Rear view

FIG. 20A. ORTHOGRAPHIC PROJECTION   FIG. 20B. PICTORIAL DRAWING

system known as "symbolic sectioning" may be used in order to show
the general type of material required. The fundamental symbols of
this system are shown in Figure 21.

Standard parts are usually indicated by "specification numbers,"
which will be explained later in this chapter.

Drafting Rules

When presenting a new idea, or when explaining some difficult prob-
lem, it is sometimes necessary for even an ordinary workman to make
a sketch which will clarify his thoughts. In this connection, the following basic rules of drafting should be kept in mind:

(1) A drawing should be dimensioned to show how a part is made—
not how it is drawn.

(2) Dimensions should be shown alongside the drawing, not on it.

(3) The drawing should be neat, well proportioned, and as detailed
as practicable.

(4) Avoid duplication of dimensions.

(5) The view of the drawing should be given—such as top view,
side elevation, profile view, etc.

(6) Material notes, names of parts, etc., should be included.

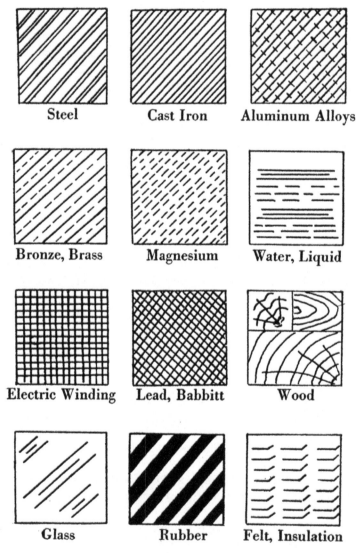

Steel   Cast Iron   Aluminum Alloys

Bronze, Brass   Magnesium   Water, Liquid

Electric Winding   Lead, Babbitt   Wood

Glass   Rubber   Felt, Insulation

Fig. 21. Symbolic Sectioning

78

Specifications

Mentioned in every airplane contract are "specifications," which set up a standard of quality for materials to be used. They cover everything from the alloy contents of rivets to the structural requirements of entire airplanes.

Specifications for private purchasers often vary—their main object being to keep the airplane within the minimum requirements of the C.A.A. "airworthiness" regulations. But when the Army or Navy— or some other governmental agency—buys an airplane, the specifications are definite and unchangeable, except in cases of extreme emergency.

Therefore, since every airplane factory does some governmental work, and since private buyers prefer materials or processes that come up to government standards, an aircraft worker should have some idea of what the latter specifications comprise. Briefly, they include:

(1) Army-Navy (AN) specifications.
(2) Army (AC) specifications.
(3) Navy (NAF) specifications.
(4) Special specifications.

The AN specifications have the top priority rating; they were created by a joint Army-Navy board to standardize the more important materials that can be used in either landplanes or seaplanes. However, since all materials can't be so classified, separate specifications— known as the AC and NAF types—are provided.

Special specifications include all materials and processes which for some reason or other have not been included in the first three groups.

A complete listing of specifications would require several books the size of this one, and would be of little value to an individual on any particular job. But there are certain standardized small parts included in the AN and AC specifications which every aircraft worker should recognize. These are listed on the accompanying specification pages.

/ Inactive for Design Purposes.
*Denotes recent change in spec.

NUMBER	NAME	NUMBER	NAME
*AN 3	Bolt-Aircraft #10	150	Turnbuckle Assy.-Fork
*AN 4	" " 1/4	AN155	Barrel - Turnbuckle
*AN 5	" " 5/16	AN160	Fork - Turnbuckle
*AN 6	" " 3/8	161	" "
*AN 7	" " 7/16	AN165	Eye - Turnbuckle for Pin
*AN 8	" " 1/2	AN170	" " Cable
*AN 9	" " 9/16	*AN200	Bearing-Air.-Heavy Duty
*AN 10	" " 5/8	*AN201	" " -Inter. Duty
*AN 12	" " 3/4	AN210	Pulley - Control
*AN 14	" " 7/8	224	Fastener - Snap
*AN 16	" " 1	225	" Curtain
*AN 23	" Clevis #10	AN226	" -Cowl-Post Type
*AN 24	" " 1/4	AN230	Grommet - Plain & Spur
*AN 25	" " 5/16	235	Hook - Lacing
*AN 26	" " 3/8	AN240	Eyelet - Lacing
*AN 27	" " 7/16	AN250	Hinge - Butt
*AN 28	" " 1/2	AN251	" Continuous
*AN 29	" " 9/16	270	Joint-Air.-Universal
*AN 30	" " 5/8	AN276	" Ball & Socket
*AN 32	" " 3/4	AN280	Key - Woodruff
*AN 34	" " 7/8	AN285	Lubricator-Pressure Type
*AN 36	" " 1	286	" " "
AN 42	" Eye 3/16 Pin #10	290	Cup - Grease
AN 43	" " 3/16 " 1/4	295	" Oil
AN 44	" " 1/4 " 5/16	300	Nail - Common Brad
AN 45	" " 5/16 " 5/16	AN301	Nail-Ft.Hd.Cement Coated
AN 46	" " 3/8 " 3/8	AN302	Pin - Escutcheon
AN 47	" " 3/8 " 7/16	303	Nail - Upholsterer's-Oval
AN 48	" " 7/16 " 1/2	AN310	Nut - Aircraft Castle
AN 49	" " 1/2 " 9/16	AN315	" " Plain
60	" Hex.Hd. Fine Thd.	AN316	" " Check
65	" " Coarse Thd.	AN320	" " Shear
70	" Carriage, with Nut	325	" Plain Hex. (Fine)
AN 73	" Drilled Hd. #10	330	" Castle (S.A.E.)
AN 74	" " " 1/4	335	" Plain Hex. (Coarse)
AN 75	" " " 5/16	AN340	" Mach. Screw
AN 76	" " " 3/8	AN345	" " " (Fine)
AN 77	Bolt-Drilled Hd. 7/16	AN350	" Wing
AN 78	" " " 1/2	AN355	" Engine - slotted
AN 79	" " " 9/16	356	Lock-Nut
AN 80	" " " 5/8	AN360	Nut - Plain - Engine
AN 81	" " " 3/4	• 364	Nut - Self Locking-Thin
AN 100	Thimble - Wire Cable	• 365	" " "
/AN110	Bushing - Cable	366	Nut Plate
AN111	" "	367	" "
AN115	Shackle - Cable	AN380	Pin - Cotter
AN130	Cable - Eye & Fork	385	" Taper
AN135	" " & Pin Eye	• 386	" Taper Threaded
AN140	" Eyes	AN392	" Flat Head 1/8

LISTING OF SPECIFICATIONS (A)

80

NUMBER	NAME	NUMBER	NAME
AN393	Pin – Flat Head 3/16	AN671	Tie Rod Strmline #6AC Std
AN394	" " " 1/4	AN671A	" " " #6SAE "
AN395	" " " 5/16	AN673	" " " #10AC "
AN396	" " " 3/8	AN673A	" " " #10SAE "
AN397	" " " 7/16	AN674	" " " 1/4AC "
AN398	" " " 1/2	AN674A	" " " 1/4SAE "
AN399	" " " 9/16	AN675	" " " 5/16AC "
AN400	" " " 5/8	AN675A	" " " 5/16SAE "
AN402	" " " 3/4	AN676	" " " 3/8AC "
AN404	" " " 7/8	AN676A	" " " 3/8SAE "
AN406	" " " 1	AN677	" " " 7/16AC "
AN415	Pin – Lock	AN677A	" " " 7/16SAE "
AN420	Rivet – C'sunk Head	AN678	" " " 1/2AC "
AN425	" " "	AN678A	" " " 1/2SAE "
AN430	" Round Head	AN679	" " " 9/16AC "
AN435	" " "	AN679A	" " " 9/16SAE "
⨍ 440	" Flat Hd. Tinners	AN680	" " " 5/8AC "
AN441	" Flat Hd.	AN680A	" " " 5/8SAE "
AN442	" " "	AN682	" " " 3/4AC "
445	" Belt, Copper	AN682A	" " " 3/4SAE "
AN450	" Tubular	AN684	" " " 7/8AC "
AN455	" Brazier Head	AN684A	" " " 7/8SAE "
AN481	Clevis–Rod End Brazing	AN686	" " " 1/AC "
AN486	" " " Adjusting	AN686A	" " " 1 SAE "
AN490	Rod End–Threaded Brazing	AN701	" " Int. #6 AC Std
500	Screw–Fil.Hd.Crse.Thd.	AN701A	" " " #6SAE "
501	" " " Fine "	AN703	" " " #10 AC "
AN502	" " " " "	AN703A	" " " #10SAE "
503	" " " Crse.	AN704	" " " 1/4 AC "
AN505	" Flat Hd.Crse.Thd.	AN704A	" " " 1/4SAE "
AN510	" " " Fine "	AN705	" " " 5/16 AC "
AN515	" Rd.Hd. Crse. Thd.	AN705A	" " " 5/16SAE "
AN520	" " " Fine "	AN706	" " " 3/8 AC "
525	" Washer Head	AN706A	" " " 3/8SAE "
AN526	" Button Head	AN707	" " " 7/16 AC "
530	" Rd.Hd. Sheet Metal	AN707A	" " " 7/16SAE "
531	" Flat Hd. " "	AN708	" " " 1/2 AC "
AN535	" Rd.Hd. Drive	AN708A	" " " 1/2SAC "
540	" Lag-Gimlet Point	735	Clamp – Bonding
AN545	" Rd. Hd. (Wood)	AN740	Clamp – Tube
AN550	" Flat Hd. (Wood)	745	" Hose
560	" Set – Sq. Hd.	750	Clip – Tube, Open Type
565	" Headless Set	755	" " Loop "
566	" " "	765	Cock – Shut Off
570	Bushing – Screw	770	Cock – Drain
650	Tag – Identification	AN771	" " Screw Type
• 660	Terminal – Electrical	AN780	Nipple – Union
AN661	" Spark Plug	AN785	Coupling-Union (Brazing)
AN665	" Tie Rod	AN790	Elbow – Union

LISTING OF SPECIFICATIONS (B)

81

NUMBER	NAME	NUMBER	NAME
791	Elbow – Union 45°	✚AN885	Hose – Fuel & Oil
AN795	Tee – Union	AN891	Cross – Primer & Gage
AN800	Cone – Union	• 892	Elbow – Hose – Oil Drain
AN805	Nut – Union	895	Fitting – Pipe
✚ 810	Fitting – Solderless	AN90C	Gasket–Annular Cop.Asb.
811	" "	905	Plug – Hex. Hd. Locking
835	Nipple–Hose, Fuel & Oil	906	" 63.Hd. L. Tapped
836	" " " "	907	" " " Locking
850	Elbow–Hose, Fuel & Oil	✚ 930	Grommet – Rubber
851	" " " " 45°	AN931	" "
852	Elbow–Hose, Fuel & Oil	AN935	Washer – Spring Lock
853	" " " " 45°	936	" Lock
860	Flange–Tube Reinforcing	940	" Burr
865	" Pipe–Riveting	945	" – Plain Com'l. Std.
866	" Strt.Thds.Rivet.	950	" Ball Socket
867	" Pipe Welding	955	" Ball Seat
868	" Strt.Thds.Welding	AN960	" Plain
AN875	Liner – Hose	AN970	" Flat for Wood
✚ 881	Hose – Cooling Liquid	975	" Taper Pin
882	" Aircraft	995	Wire – Lock
		AN996	Ring – Lock

Listing of Specifications (C)

The AN numbers presented here designate the page upon which pertinent specifications will be found in the "AN parts book," a copy of which may be obtained at any aircraft factory for reference purposes. Actually, there are a number of different specifications on each page of the parts book for different sizes and types of the parts listed here.

The size and composition of an AN part is usually designated by "dash numbers." For example, take AN 505. On a blueprint this might be listed as AN 505–6–10. That would mean, first of all, that a flat-head screw with coarse thread is required (since page 505 of the AN parts book is devoted exclusively to such parts). It would also mean that the screw should be of steel; otherwise, the listing would be AN 505B (for brass) or AN 505D (for dural). The dash number 6 indicates the desired thread size—which in this case would be 6 coarse (6–32)—and the dash number 10 indicates the desired length in terms of sixteenths of an inch (or, in other words, $^{10}\!/_{16}$ inch).

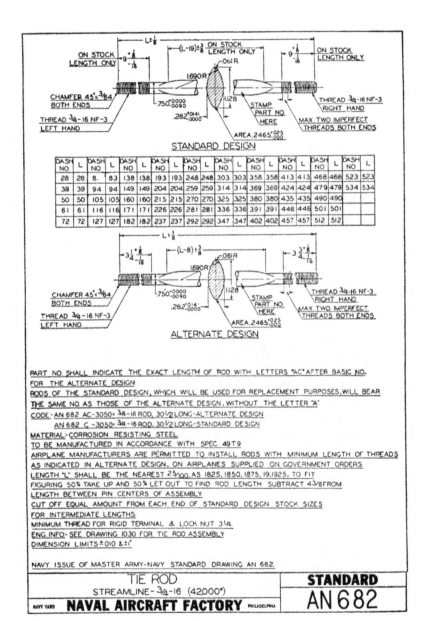

STANDARD DESIGN

DASH NO	L	DASH NO	L	DASH NO	L	DASH NO	L	DASH NO	L	DASH NO	L	DASH NO	L	DASH NO	L	DASH NO	L	DASH NO	L
28	28	8.	83	138	138	193	193	248	248	303	303	358	358	413	413	468	468	523	523
38	39	94	94	149	149	204	204	259	259	314	314	369	369	424	424	479	479	534	534
50	50	105	105	160	160	215	215	270	270	325	325	380	380	435	435	490	490		
61	61	116	116	171	171	226	226	281	281	336	336	391	391	446	446	501	501		
72	72	127	127	182	182	237	237	292	292	347	347	402	402	457	457	512	512		

ALTERNATE DESIGN

PART NO. SHALL INDICATE THE EXACT LENGTH OF ROD WITH LETTERS "AC" AFTER BASIC NO.
FOR THE ALTERNATE DESIGN
RODS OF THE STANDARD DESIGN, WHICH WILL BE USED FOR REPLACEMENT PURPOSES, WILL BEAR
THE SAME NO. AS THOSE OF THE ALTERNATE DESIGN, WITHOUT THE LETTER "A"
CODE - AN 682 AC-3050: ¾-16 ROD, 30½ LONG-ALTERNATE DESIGN
        AN 682 C -3050: ¾-16 ROD, 30½ LONG-STANDARD DESIGN
MATERIAL:- CORROSION RESISTING STEEL
TO BE MANUFACTURED IN ACCORDANCE WITH SPEC. 49 T 9.
AIRPLANE MANUFACTURERS ARE PERMITTED TO INSTALL RODS WITH MINIMUM LENGTH OF THREADS
AS INDICATED IN ALTERNATE DESIGN, ON AIRPLANES SUPPLIED ON GOVERNMENT ORDERS.
LENGTH "L" SHALL BE THE NEAREST 25/100, AS 18.25, 18.50, 18.75, 19, 19.25, TO FIT
FIGURING 50% TAKE UP AND 50% LET OUT. TO FIND ROD LENGTH SUBTRACT 4⅜ FROM
LENGTH BETWEEN PIN CENTERS OF ASSEMBLY.
CUT OFF EQUAL AMOUNT FROM EACH END OF STANDARD DESIGN STOCK SIZES
FOR INTERMEDIATE LENGTHS.
MINIMUM THREAD FOR RIGID TERMINAL & LOCK NUT 3¼.
ENG. INFO - SEE DRAWING 1030 FOR TIE ROD ASSEMBLY.
DIMENSION LIMITS ± 010 & ± 1°

NAVY ISSUE OF MASTER ARMY-NAVY STANDARD DRAWING AN 682.

TIE ROD	STANDARD
STREAMLINE- ¾-16 (42,000°)	
NAVY YARD NAVAL AIRCRAFT FACTORY PHILADELPHIA	AN 682

SAMPLE PAGE FROM AN PARTS BOOK

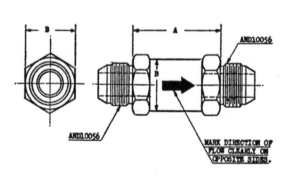

AND10056

AND10056

MARK DIRECTION OF FLOW CLEARLY ON OPPOSITE SIDES.

AN PART NO.	TUBE O. D.	RATED FLOW CAPACITY G.P.M.	A ±1/32	B
AN6207-4	1/4	1.2	1-17/32	.688 +.0025 -.004
AN6207-5	5/16	2.3	1-3/4	.750 +.0025 -.004
AN6207-6	3/8	3.5	1-3/4	.813 +.0025 -.004
AN6207-8	1/2	6.0	2-7/32	1.000 +.0025 -.004
AN6207-12	3/4	16.0	2-3/4	1.375 +.003 -.005
AN6207-16	1	29.0	3-5/16	1.625 ±.005

REVISED

APPROVED 7-11-42

DIMENSIONS IN INCHES.
THIS DRAWING AND THE SPECIFICATION COMPLEMENT ONE ANOTHER, AND TOGETHER
COMPLETELY DEFINE THIS PRODUCT.

SAMPLE PAGE FROM AN PARTS BOOK

SIZE (INCH)	ALLOY NUMBER		SIZE (INCH)	ALLOY NUMBER	
	17ST	24ST		17ST	24ST
3/16	X	X	1-1/4	X	X
1/4	X	X	1-3/8	X	X
5/16	X	X	1-1/2	X	X
3/8	X	X	1-5/8		X
7/16	X	X	1-3/4	X	X
1/2	X	·X	1-7/8		X
9/16	X	X	2	X	X
5/8	X	X	* 2-1/4	X	X
11/16		X	* 2-1/2	X	X
3/4	X	X	* 2-3/4	X	X
13/16		X	* 3	X	X
7/8	X	X	3-1/4	X	X
15/16		·X	3-1/2	X	X
1	X	X	3-3/4	X	X
1-1/8	X	X	4	X	X

X = STANDARD SIZES OF SQUARE BAR.   T (AS IN 24ST) = HEAT TREATED.

* = PRODUCED AS EXTRUSIONS.

LENGTH: 12 FEET IS STANDARD LENGTH FOR 2" SQUARE BAR AND FOR SMALLER SIZES. IF ACCEPTABLE TO THE PRODUCER, THIS PRODUCT MAY BE SPECIFIED IN "MILL LENGTHS" AND EACH SIZE WILL BE IN ONE SINGLE LENGTH FROM 8 TO 18 FT. REGARDLESS OF LENGTH SPECIFIED, A PERCENTAGE BY WEIGHT OF ANY SIZE MAY BE INCLUDED IN RANDOM LENGTHS AS FOLLOWS:

SIZE	STANDARD LENGTH SPECIFIED	MILL LENGTH SPECIFIED
UNDER 2"	20% FROM 8 TO 12 FT.	15% FROM 8 TO 16 FT.
3-1/4"	100% FROM 6 TO 18 FT.	15% FROM 6 TO 18 FT.
3-1/2" AND OVER	100% FROM 3 TO 18 FT.	15% FROM 3 TO 18 FT.

REVISED

APPROVED 10-16-42

ARMY-NAVY AERONAUTICAL DESIGN STANDARD	AND10131
ALUMINUM BAR - STANDARD ALLOYS, TEMPER AND SIZES OF SQUARE	

SAMPLE PAGE FROM AN PARTS BOOK

THICK-NESS (INCHES)	WIDTH (INCHES)																					
	3/8	7/16	1/2	5/8	3/4	7/8	1	1-1/4	1-1/2	1-3/4	2	2-1/4	2-1/2	2-3/4	3	3-1/2	4	4-1/2	5	6	8	10
1/8	X		X	X	X	X	X	X	X	X	X	X	X	X	X							
3/16	X	X	X	X	X	X	X	X	X	X	X	X	X	X	X							
1/4	X		X	X	X	X	X	X	X	X	X	X	X	X	X	X	X		X	X		
5/16	X		X	X	X	X	X	X	X	X	X	X	X	X	X		X			X		X
3/8		X	X	X	X	X	X	X	X	X	X	X	X	X	X	X	X			X		X
7/16		X	X	X	X	X	X	X	X	X	X	X	X	X	X							
1/2			X	X	X	X	X	X	X	X	X	X	X	X	X	X	X			T	X	X
9/16				X	X	X	X	X	X	X	X	X	X	X	X							
5/8				X	X	X	X	X	X	X	X	X	X	X	X	X	X			X		X
3/4					X	X	X	X	X	X	X	X	X	X	X	X	X			X	X	X
7/8					X	X	X	X	X	X	X	X	X	X	X	X				X		X
1							X	X	X	X	X	X	X	X	X	X				X	X	X
1-1/8								X	X	X	X	X	X		X	X	X					X
1-1/4								X	X	X	X	X	X		X	X	X			X	X	X
1-3/8								X	X	X	X	X	X		X	X	X			X		X
1-1/2									X	X	X	X	X	X	X	X			X	X	X	X
1-3/4												X	X	X	X				X	X	X	X
2												X	X	X	X	X	X	X	X	X	X	X
2-1/4															X	X	X	X				
2-1/2															X	X	X	X				
2-3/4															X		X	X				
3															X		X	X				

X = STANDARD SIZES OF RECTANGULAR BAR.   T (IN 24ST) = HEAT TREATED.

CONDITION: 24ST IS THE ONLY STANDARD ALLOY AND TEMPER FOR RECTANGULAR BAR.

FINISH: UNLESS OTHERWISE SPECIFIED, SIZES ON LEFT OF DOUBLE LINE ARE COLD FINISHED, AND THOSE ON RIGHT ARE ROLLED.

APPROVED 10-16-42   REVISED

ARMY-NAVY AERONAUTICAL DESIGN STANDARD

ALUMINUM BAR - STANDARD ALLOY AND TEMPER (24ST), AND SIZES OF RECTANGULAR

AND10132

SAMPLE PAGE FROM AN PARTS BOOK

Since the dash numbering system for each AN part differs, there is only one way for a person to determine the various designations—and that is by referring to the parts book itself.

A careful study of the sample pages from the AN parts book should enable the reader to tackle the parts book at a later date without serious difficulties.

Bolts and Screws

The most important thing about a bolt or screw is its thread. Thread nomenclature is shown in Figure 22.

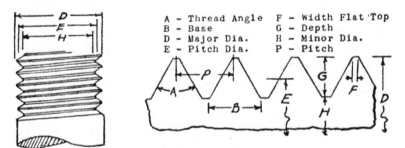

```
A - Thread Angle    F - Width Flat 'Top
B - Base            G - Depth
D - Major Dia.      H - Minor Dia.
E - Pitch Dia.      P - Pitch
```

FIG. 22. AMERICAN NATIONAL STANDARD THREAD

Threads on both aircraft bolts and machine screws are usually of the American National Standard type, which includes three groups: (1) national coarse or NC, (2) national fine or NF, and (3) national extra-fine or N. The NF thread is commonly known as S.A.E. standard and is used on all AN bolts, unless otherwise specified. NC thread is commonly known as the U.S. standard, and is frequently used on both aircraft bolts and machine screws.

While the general dimensions of the above three groups of threads vary, they come in equivalent sizes, depending on their respective diameters; they differ in accordance with the number of threads per inch. For example, a size number 1 NC threaded bolt would have 64 threads per inch, while a size number 1 NF threaded bolt would have 72 threads per inch.

American National Standard threads have four classes of fits: (1) loose, (2) free, (3) medium, and (4) close. The class 3 or medium fit is most popular in aircraft work.

AN bolts are usually made of cadmium-plated nickel steel or 24ST anodized dural. Nickel steel is indicated by an X or similar mark on the head of the bolt, while dural is indicated by two small dashes. The main thing to remember in using a bolt is never to use a size which will allow part of the thread to extend into the material.

The common names of both bolts and screws usually depend on their respective head characteristics. Hence, a hex-head bolt has a head with six-sides—shaped like a "hexagon." And, if there is a safety wire hole in the head, it is a drilled hex-head bolt. A fillister-head screw has a thick body and head, which forms a sort of "fillister" joint. A flat-head screw is the possessor of a flat, countersunk head. A round-head screw has a definitely rounded head, while a button-head screw has a somewhat rounded head that looks like a rather thin button.

Like all other parts of an airplane, each bolt and each screw is designed for a very definite purpose. The primary objective of a clevis bolt is to resist shear (or side) forces; a thick-headed bolt reacts best against longitudinal forces, etc. Similarly, fine threads are best in parts exposed to excessive vibrations while coarse threads generally afford the most structural strength.

A screw differs from a bolt in that it has no appreciable "grip," or shank. The grip is the blank space between the head and threads of a bolt. Hence, the threads of a screw always extend inside the material.

Only the clevis bolt has a screwdriver ridge on its head; all screws have such ridges and their construction is usually more delicate than that of a bolt. Cadmium-plated carbon steel is generally considered the best material for aircraft machine screws.

Nuts and Washers

Dural, brass, and steel are the most common materials for nuts used in aircraft work—steel being most popular. Steel nuts are cadmium plated while dural nuts are anodized. The accompanying drawings

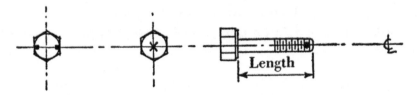

AN 3 to AN 16—Hex-head Bolt

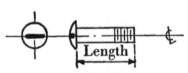

AN 23 to AN 36—Clevis Bolt

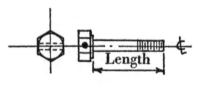

AN 73 to AN 81—Drilled Hex-head
Bolt

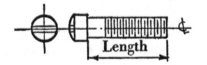

AN 502—Fillister-head Screw

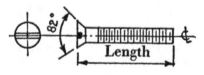

AN 505 and AN 510—Flat-head
Screw

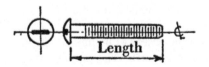

AN 515 and AN 520—Round-head
Screw

AN 526—Button-head Screw

FIG. 23. AN BOLTS AND SCREWS

indicate some of the AN and AC nuts used daily by the American aircraft industry.

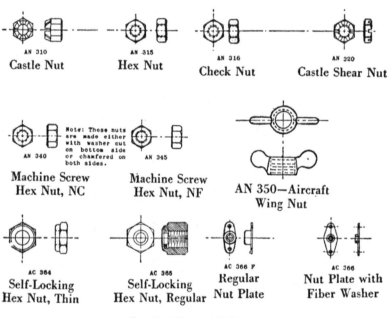

FIG. 24. AN AND AC NUTS

The castle nut, which gets its name as a result of its shape, is probably the most widely used aircraft nut. It is used on bolts with cotter-pin holes drilled through their threads—the notches on the nut providing a firm grip on the cotter pin.

Aircraft washers are made from a wide variety of materials—steel, dural, brass, pure aluminum, fiber, and so forth. The purpose of a washer is to supplement the work of a nut and bolt, or of a nut and screw, by distributing the clamping load over a greater area—to prevent the gouging of material under the nut, bolt, or screw head. When insulation between dissimilar metals is required, fiber and pure aluminum washers are preferred.

The more popular AN and AC washers are shown in Figure 25.

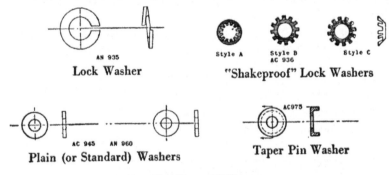

AN 935
Lock Washer

Style A Style B
AC 936 Style C

"Shakeproof" Lock Washers

AC 945   AN 960
Plain (or Standard) Washers

AC975
Taper Pin Washer

FIG. 25. AN AND AC WASHERS

Turnbuckle Assemblies

Aeronautically, the turnbuckle is best known as a "wire-tightener," used on control wires or cables. Its assembly often comprises S.A.E. 2330 steel parts, including a barrel and two "ends." These ends, which are attached to the wire or cable, may be either a "fork" (AN 161) or eye-bolt (AN 170) attachment.

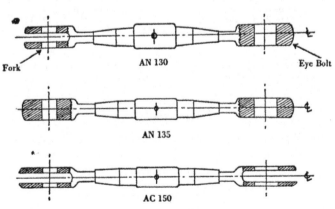

Fork   AN 130   Eye Bolt

AN 135

AC 150

FIG. 26. DESIGN CHARACTERISTICS OF TURNBUCKLE ASSEMBLIES

Threads inside the barrel are turned in opposite directions; this gives the turnbuckle a tightening or loosening effect, as circumstances require.

Turnbuckle assemblies are made in a considerable range of thread sizes, any one of which may be a "long" or "short" assembly. Figure 26 shows the design characteristics of three typical assemblies.

Class 3 NF threads are most popular in turnbuckles, and all parts of the assembly are usually cadmium plated.

Further data regarding turnbuckle parts and assemblies will be found in the following table:

SIZE & THREADS	STRENGTH P.S.I.	**ASSEMBLY LENGTH AN130, 135,140	**ASSEMBLY LENGTH AN150	BARREL LENGTH
** 6-40	800	4-1/2	–	2-1/4
**10-32	1600	4-1/2	4-1/2	2-1/4
**12-28	2100	4-1/2	4-9/16	2-1/4
1/4-28	3200	4-1/2	4-11/16	2-1/4
5/16-24	4600	4-1/2	4-17/16	2-1/4
**10-32	1600	8	8	4
**12-28	2100	8	8-1/16	4
1/4-28	3200	8	8-7/32	4
5/16-24	4600	8	8-5/16	4
3/8-24	6100	8	8-9/16	4
3/8-24	8000	8	8-5/8	4
7/16-20	12500	9	9-1/8	4-1/4
1/2-20	17500	9-1/2	9-5/8	4-1/4

* Assembly lengths are given from center of hole in one end to center of hole in the other end when threads are flush with ends of barrel.

Control Pulleys

A control pulley is a small wheel, revolving on an axle, with a groove cut in its circumference for the purpose of guiding the movements of a control wire or cable. Hard, fibrous materials (sometimes plastics) are often used in control pulleys because they will not harm metal wire or cable.

Figure 27 shows the general contours of a control pulley.

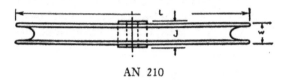

AN 210

Fig. 27. Control Pulley

Sizes and fits of control pulleys are shown in the following table:

L	W	J	FITS CABLE	SIZE
1.25	.250	.297	1/16 – 5/64	– 3/32
2.5	.250	.297	1/16 – 5/64	– 3/32
2	.422	.484	1/8 – 5/32	– 3/16
3.5	.422	.484	1/8 – 5/32	– 3/16
5	.500	.620	3/16 – 7/32	– 1/4
6	.500	.620	3/16 – 7/32	– 1/4
10	.875	1.125	5/16 – 3/8	– 7/16
14.5	1.000	1.245	7/16 – 1/2	–

Cotter Pins

The purpose of a cotter pin usually is to hold a nut in place, preventing it from working loose when exposed to vibrations. Cotter pins come in a wide variety of sizes; but their contours are almost invariably the same. Figure 28 shows a typical AN cotter pin and how it should be used.

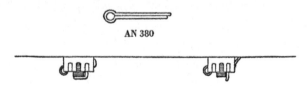

AN 380

Fig. 28. AN Cotter Pin; Correct Use (left) and Incorrect (right)

A cotter pin should never touch the metal beneath a nut. The bent portion of the pin should point either toward the tail of the airplane, or toward the ground. If the pin is too long, it should be cut down. If you can move it with your finger, it should be replaced. Never use the same pin twice.

Taper Pins

Used largely as wedges and supports of various sorts, taper pins come in two classes—one with threads, and the other without threads. The threaded type may or may not include a cotter-pin hole. Both types are usually made of cadmium-plated nickel steel. Typical specimens are shown in Figure 29.

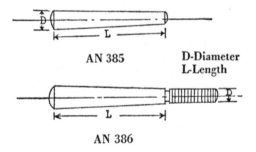

AN 385   D-Diameter
             L-Length

AN 386

FIG. 29. TAPER PINS

Dzus Fasteners

One of the more widely used aircraft parts that are not covered by government specifications is the Dzus self-locking fastener. This part

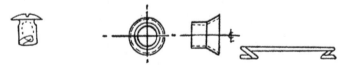

FIG. 30. DZUS SELF-LOCKING FASTENER: (LEFT TO RIGHT) FASTENER, GROMMET, SPRING

is made in a variety of sizes and is used for fastening cowlings, fairings, hand-hole covers, inspection plates, and so forth. Its three main parts are shown in Figure 30.

The chief merit of the Dzus fastener is the fact that it can be put on or taken off in a matter of seconds without a loss of strength or

FIG. 31. ASSEMBLY OF DZUS FASTENER

holding efficiency. Installed, the Dzus assembly appears as shown in Figure 31.

All parts of the Dzus assembly are made of steel, except for the grommet, which is dural. Several designs are used in making these component parts, but the general appearance and purpose of each is

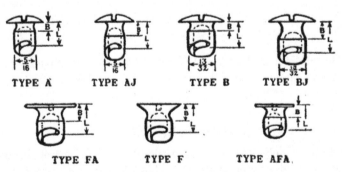

FIG. 32. TYPES OF DZUS FASTENER

the same. The table on page 96 lists the appropriate fastener symbol numbers and measurements along with suitable grommet and spring numbers.

DZUS FASTENER SYMBOL NUMBERS AND MEASUREMENTS

Fastener Size No.	L.	B.	Grommet Size	Spring Size
A-30	0.300	0.100	375	100
A-35	.350	.100	375	100
A-40	.400	.100	375	100
B-40	.400	.125	500	200
B-50	.500	.125	500	200
F-50	.500	.234	502	1375
FA-46	.460	.250	502	1375
FA-56	.560	.250	502	1375
FA-66	.660	.250	502	1375
AJ-35	.350	.125	375	100
AJ-40	.400	.190	375	100
AJ-45	.450	.190	375	100
BJ-40	.400	.188	500	200
BJ-50	.500	.250	500	200
AFA-35	.350	.188	375F	100F
AFA-40	.400	.188	375F	100F
AFA-45	.450	.188	375F	100F
AFA-50	0.500	0.188	375F	100F

The letters A, B, F, FA, etc., in this table denote the fastener type; the abbreviations L. and B. indicate dimensions. These are shown in the drawings of Figure 32.

Dill Lok-Skru Fastener

Another widely used aircraft part that has not as yet been included in government specifications is the Lok-Skru fastener produced by the Dill Manufacturing Company of Cleveland, Ohio. This fastener is used for "blind" attachments—that is, in places where it is impossible to apply a regular nut to a bolt or screw.

The complete Lok-Skru assembly consists of a "head" and a "barrel," whose purpose is to provide a sort of stationary nut or set of threads into which an attaching screw can be inserted. The three head types, and their general appearance when assembled, are shown in Figure 33.

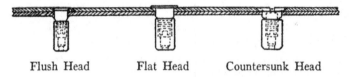

Flush Head   Flat Head   Countersunk Head

FIG. 33. TYPES OF LOK-SKRU ASSEMBLY

Lok-Skru fasteners are made of both steel and dural in the sizes shown in the following table:

HEAD TYPE	STEEL			DURAL		
Flush	6–32,	8–32,	10–32	6–32,	8–32,	10–24
Flat	6–32,	8–32,	10–32	6–32,	8–32,	10–24
Countersunk	6–32,	8–32,	10–32	6–32		

The sizes in this table indicate the dimensions and threads of the attachment screw as well as the assembly proper. The length of the head of a fastener depends on the thickness of the material at the point where the installation is to be made; the mechanic should consult his blueprint or factory specification book for this information.

Drill sizes necessary for installing Lok-Skru fasteners are shown in the table on page 98.[1]

Closely related to the regular Lok-Skru fasteners is the Dill Hexagon Lok-Skru fastener, especially designed for gas tanks and other tight installations; it is called the "type D fastener." Steel, dural, and bronze are used in making heads for this type and, with but one exception, the barrels are made in one size only—necessitating a $1\frac{7}{64}$ (.265) drill for all but countersunk installations. When countersunk installations are made, drill sizes are in conformity with those given in the table.

---

[1] When the countersunk fastener is installed, the metal should be "dimpled" in a manner that will be explained later in this book.

DRILL SIZES FOR LOK-SKRU FASTENERS

DRILL	SCREW SIZE	HEAD	Sheet Thickness				
			.020	.030	.040	.053	.065
			Size of Hole to Drill in Flat Sheet.				
19/64	10-32	Steel-Flat					
	10-32	Steel-Flush	#A	#D	#D	1/4	19/64
	10-32	Steel-Csk.					
	10-24	Dural-Flat	.234	.246	.246	.250	.297
.297	10-24	Dural-Flush					
	8-32	Dural-Flat					
	8-32	Dural-Flush					
17/64	8-32	Steel-Flat					
	8-32	Steel-Flush	#3	#3	#1	#A	#D
	8-32	Steel-Csk.					
.265	6-32	Dural-Flat	.213	.213	.228	.234	.246
	6-32	Dural-Flush					
	6-32	Dural-Csk.					
15/64	6-32	Steel-Flat	#10	#7	#5	#3	#1
	6-32	Steel-Flush					
.234	6-32	Steel-Csk.	.1935	.201	.2055	.213	.228

Features of the type D fastener are shown in Figure 34.

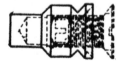

FIG. 34. TYPE D FASTENER, SHOWING COMPLETE AS-
SEMBLY AND COUNTERSUNK HEAD

Explosive Rivets

Explosive rivets were first developed in Germany in 1936. They have since been improved and used extensively in the American aircraft industry.

Several types are in use at present, all working on the general principle shown in Figure 35.

The explosive charge in one of these rivets is approximately equivalent to that of a cap in a toy pistol. It is set off by a single blow on the "lock rod," causing a "back swelling" in the rivet. This so-called back swelling gives the rivet a very strong, tight grip; and the lock rod, true to its name, remains fixed inside the rivet.

Annealed aluminum alloys generally comprise the body of the explosive rivet, which is used only in spots that are inaccessible to a bucking bar.

Except for inherent structural differences, the explosive rivet is stronger than a normal rivet; this is because the former can be applied

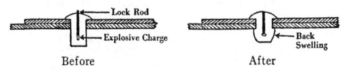

Before   After

FIG. 35. EXPLOSIVE RIVETS

in a single operation, whereas the latter often requires dozens of blows which tend to break down its metallic structure.

Further data on rivets will be found in Chapter 7.

Goodrich Riv-Nuts

The Goodrich Riv-Nut is a hollow threaded rivet-nut, frequently used for the attachment of rubber "de-icer" boots to the leading edges of wings and tail sections. Like the Lok-Skru fasteners and explosive rivets, they can be installed while working entirely on one side of a piece of material.

Made of 53S material, heat treated and anodized, Riv-Nuts come in three sizes—6–32, 8–32, 10–32—and four head types, as shown in Figure 36.

Briefly, the Riv-Nut acts as a sort of nut plate for the attachment of accessories or fixtures. To keep it from turning in the hole after being installed, a small key is provided, as shown in the illustration of the flat-head type; this key fits in a notch cut in the side of the hole.

Sometimes a Riv-Nut may be used only as a rivet. When this is done, the key should be omitted and a headless plug should be inserted into the threads to seal the hole.

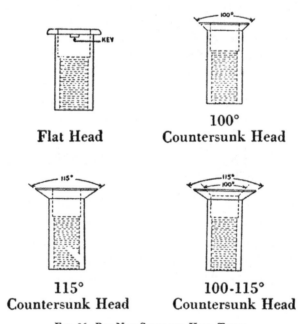

Flat Head

100°
Countersunk Head

115°
Countersunk Head

100-115°
Countersunk Head

FIG. 36. RIV-NUT SIZES AND HEAD TYPES

Special Riv-Nuts with closed ends may be used in sealed compartments, etc. However, the open-end type is generally preferred because it is lighter and will not become plugged with dirt and other extraneous matter.

Typical Riv-Nut installations are shown in Figure 37.

Dimpled Csk   Machine Csk   Flat Head

FIG. 37. RIV-NUT INSTALLATIONS

A fractional part of a fuselage section is shown here. Note the rivets, tubing, and other AN parts that have been installed. (*Consolidated Photo*)

Above. With steel measuring scales, these men are lining up fuselage sections for a B-24D land bomber. (*Consolidated Aircraft Corp. Photo*)

Below. Tail turrets for the new B-17F Flying Fortress bombers are lined up receiving final installations before being attached to the fuselage. (*Boeing Aircraft Co. Photo*)

Riv-Nut plug screws are represented by two types (see Figure 38).

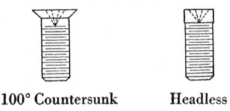

100° Countersunk   Headless

FIG. 38. RIV-NUT PLUG SCREWS

The countersunk plug screw is used when a regular attachment screw is not required. Both types of plug screws come in three sizes—6–32, 8–32, and 10–32.

Measuring Instruments

Measurements are of especial importance to the aircraft industry because every part, large or small, must be an exact size in order to function properly. Sometimes a miscalculation of less than one-sixteenth of an inch can cause an entire airplane to be rejected before it is flown.

The American standard of length is one foot, but in aircraft work the inch and fractional parts thereof are mentioned most frequently. "Fractional parts thereof" may include measurements as slight as one ten-thousandth of an inch.

The *rule* is the most frequently used measuring instrument in any type of engineering work. Ordinary rules are divided into minimum measurements of one-sixteenth of an inch; this is the familiar wooden type. Engineering rules (or "scales") are made of steel and divided into minimum measurements of one thirty-second and one sixty-fourth of an inch. Virtually all surface measurements can be made with the rule, or its close relation the steel measuring tape.

Scribers and dividers usually accompany the scale or measuring tape in making measurements. The scriber is a steel pointed instrument which will leave appropriate marks on the material being measured. The divider is a compass attachment for the scriber, used for indicating circles and arcs.

Hermaphrodite or "Jenny" calipers are similar to the divider, but are used exclusively for such jobs as centering a bar or determining edge distances (for rivets, etc.) as shown in Figure 39.

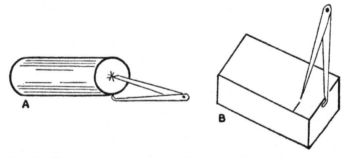

FIG. 39. HERMAPHRODITE CALIPER; CENTERING A BAR (*A*), MARKING EDGE DISTANCE (*B*)

Thickness gages are of particular interest to inspectors, since they are so valuable in locating high rivet heads and clearances between other parts. Most common of the thickness gages is the "feeler set" (see Figure 40).

FIG. 40. "FEELER SET" THICKNESS GAGE

The numbers on the blades of the feeler gages indicate the blade thickness in terms of thousandths of an inch. Thus, blade eight will

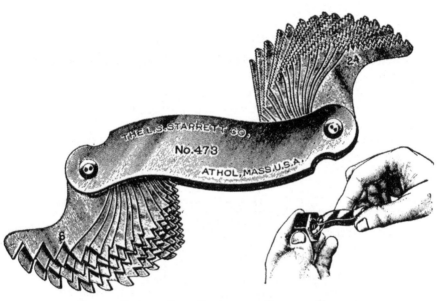

FIG. 41. GAGE FOR BOTH INTERNAL AND EXTERNAL THREADS
(Courtesy of the L. S. Starrett Co.)

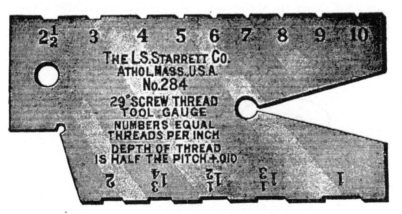

FIG. 42. STANDARD SCREW THREAD GAGE
(Courtesy of the L. S. Starrett Co.)

103

determine clearances of eight thousandths of an inch, when inserted in a gap.

Thread gages are used to determine the pitch and other measurements of threads. Two frequently used instruments of this type are indicated in Figures 41 and 42.

Depth gages are often used in aircraft work, and the most common type is that of the rule with the sliding head (Figure 43).

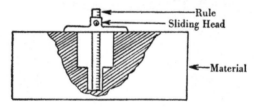

FIG. 43. DEPTH GAGE

Ring and plug gages are sometimes used by inspectors in aircraft work. The plug gage is precisely what its name implies—that is, a plug which will determine whether holes or slots have been correctly proportioned. Ring gages serve the same purpose when dealing with rods, bars, and so forth. The size of either a ring or plug gage depends on each individual job. These gages may be distinguished by the characteristics shown in Figures 44 and 45.

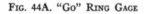

FIG. 44A. "Go" RING GAGE   FIG. 44B. "NOT GO" RING GAGE

Note the use of the terms "Go" and "Not Go." The "Go" plug or ring should fit into or upon the perfectly made part; the "Not Go" gages will fit only parts that are improperly made. The "Go" and

"Not Go" dimensions are usually noted on the plug and ring gages; this is a simple method of avoiding confusion.

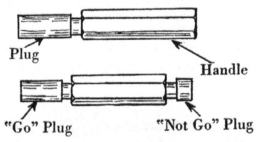

Fig. 45. Plug Gages

Micrometers are the most popular of the precision instruments used in the aircraft industry. The conventional micrometer can make measurements of as little as one thousandth of an inch.

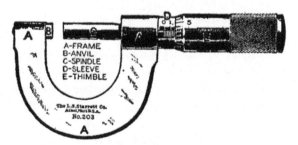

A-FRAME
B-ANVIL
C-SPINDLE
D-SLEEVE
E-THIMBLE

The L.S.Starrett Co.
Atbol,Mass.U.S.A.
No.203

Fig. 46. Typical Micrometer
(Courtesy of the L. S. Starrett Co.)

The micrometer shown in Figure 46 is often used for such purposes as determining the thickness of sheet metal. To use this instrument, first turn the thimble (*E*) until its zero graduation coincides with the zero graduation of the sleeve (*D*). At this point, the anvil (*B*) and the spindle (*C*) should be in contact with one another; otherwise, the micrometer has not been adjusted properly.

Now turn the thimble back one complete revolution, and note how its edge is graduated into twenty-five divisions. Each of these divisions represents one-thousandth of an inch (.001"). Therefore, when the thimble has been turned one complete revolution to the first graduation on the sleeve, we have a measurement of 25-thousandths of an inch (.025"). Thus, we know that each crossline on the sleeve represents .025".

Reaching the figure "1" on the sleeve requires four complete revolutions of the thimble. Since each revolution is equal to 25-thousandths

FIG. 47. MICROMETER THREAD GAGE
(Courtesy of Brown & Sharpe Mfg. Co.)

of an inch, the figure "1" would therefore represent 100-thousandths of an inch (.100").

The simplest way to read a micrometer is to imagine you are making change. Let the graduations on the thimble equal *cents;* the crosslines on the sleeve, *quarters;* and the figures on the sleeve, *dollars.*

Thus, let us assume we are measuring the thickness of a piece of sheet metal and obtain the reading shown in Figure 46. The figure on the sleeve shows us that we have one dollar, the three additional graduations (quarters) indicate 75 cents, and the marks on the thimble show another 3 cents—making a total of $1.78. Translated as a fraction of an inch, this would give us .178" as the thickness of our sheet metal.

The micrometer should fit snugly over the object that is being measured, but it should never be tightened so as to cause the anvil or spindle to make an impression on the object. For Decimal and Metric Equivalents used in taking measurements with micrometers and other instruments, see the Appendix.

All micrometers may be read by observing the handle instructions and following the general procedure outlined in this section. Some less common types of these instruments are shown in Figures 47 and 48.

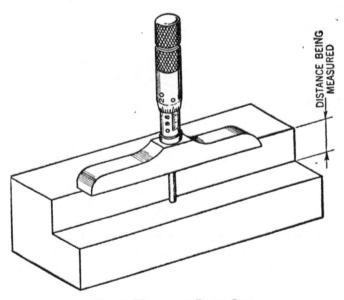

Fig. 48. Micrometer Depth Gage

Bending Allowances

When a piece of metal is bent, it stretches on the outside and shrinks on the inside—the amount of distortion depending on the abruptness of the bend. Therefore, in order to form a perfect part without wasting material, a workman should be able to calculate the amount of metal he will require for various curved parts.

In dealing with light gauge metals, such as are most frequently used

in aircraft work, the empirical formula has proved to be the most satisfactory method of determining bending allowances. This formula is
based entirely upon experience, and cannot be mathematically proved.
Its basic form is:

Degree of Bend $\times$ [(.01743 $\times$ Radius) + (.0078 $\times$ Thickness)]
= Bending Allowance

The terms of this empirical formula are shown in Figure 49.

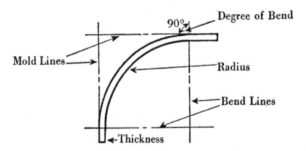

FIG. 49. REPRESENTATION OF EMPIRICAL FORMULA

To find the allowance for a 90-degree bend, such as is illustrated
here, the radius and thickness must first be ascertained. A micrometer
will reveal the thickness, and the radius can be determined approximately as follows:

1 $\times$ thickness on SO material
2½ $\times$ thickness on ST material
3 $\times$ thickness on SRT material

As an example, let us assume that the material in the drawing has
a thickness of .040 inch and a radius of .125 inch. The bending allowance could then be calculated as follows:

T (Thickness) = .040
R (Radius) = .125
D (Degree of Bend) = 90°
BA = Bend Allowance

Therefore:

.01743	.0078	.00217875
×.125	×.040	+.00031200
8715	.0003120	.00249075 = 1° Bend
3486		
1743		
.00217875		

$$.00249075$$
$$×90°$$
$$.22416750 = BA$$

Reducing *BA* to simpler terms, we get .224 or ¼ inch as our answer. The table below, derived from the empirical formula, shows the more common allowances for one-degree bends in aluminum alloys:

THICKNESS OF METAL IN INCHES							
RADII	.022	.032	.040	.051	.064	.091	.128	.187
1/32	.00072	.00079	.00086	.00094	.00104	.00125	.00154	.00200
1/16	.00126	.00135	.00140	.00149	.00159	.00180	.00209	.00255
3/32	.00180	.00188	.00195	.00203	.00213	.00234	.00263	.00309
1/8	.00235	.00243	.00249	.00258	.00268	.00289	.00317	.00364
5/32	.00290	.00297	.00304	.00312	.00322	.00343	.00372	.00418
3/16	.00344	.00352	.00358	.00367	.00377	.00398	.00426	.00473
7/32	.00398	.00406	.00412	.00421	.00431	.00452	.00481	.00527
1/4	.00454	.00461	.00467	.00476	.00486	.00507	.00535	.00582
9/32	.00507	.00515	.00521	.00530	.00540	.00561	.00590	.00636
5/16	.00562	.00570	.00576	.00584	.00595	.00616	.00644	.00691
11/32	.00616	.00624	.00630	.00639	.00649	.00670	.00699	.00745
3/8	.00671	.00679	.00685	.00693	.00704	.00725	.00753	.00800
13/32	.00725	.00733	.00739	.00748	.00758	.00779	.00808	.00854
7/16	.00780	.00787	.00794	.00802	.00812	.00834	.00862	.00908
15/32	.00834	.00842	.00848	.00857	.00867	.00888	.00917	.00963
1/2	.00889	.00896	.00903	.00911	.00921	.00943	.00971	.01017
17/32	.00943	.00951	.00957	.00966	.00976	.00997	.01025	.01072
9/16	.00998	.01005	.01012	.01020	.01030	.01051	.01080	.01126
19/32	.01051	.01058	.01065	.01073	.01083	.01105	.01133	.01179
5/8	.01107	.01114	.01121	.01129	.01139	.01160	.01189	.01235
21/32	.01161	.01170	.01175	.01183	.01193	.01214	.01245	.01289
11/16	.01216	.01223	.01230	.01238	.01248	.01268	.01298	.01344
23/32	.01269	.01276	.01283	.01291	.01301	.01322	.01351	.01397
3/4	.01324	.01332	.01338	.01347	.01357	.01378	.01407	.01453
25/32	.01378	.01386	.01391	.01401	.01411	.01432	.01461	.01507
13/16	.01433	.01441	.01447	.01456	.01466	.01487	.01516	.01562
27/32	.01487	.01494	.01501	.01509	.01519	.01540	.01569	.01615
7/8	.01542	.01550	.01556	.01565	.01575	.01596	.01625	.01671
29/32	.01596	.01604	.01610	.01619	.01629	.01650	.01679	.01727
15/16	.01651	.01659	.01665	.01674	.01684	.01705	.01734	.01780
31/32	.01705	.01712	.01718	.01727	.01737	.01758	.01788	.01833
1	.01760	.01768	.01774	.01783	.01793	.01814	.01843	.01889

Another method of calculating bending allowances is the "Set-Back" or "J" chart (see Figure 50).

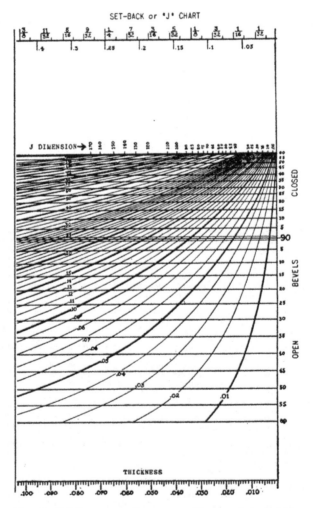

FIG. 50. "J" CHART FOR CALCULATING BENDING ALLOWANCES

Set-back is shown in Figure 51 as the difference between the amount of material required to form the angle *DGE* and the arc *C*.

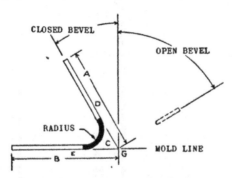

FIG. 51. INDICATION OF SET-BACK

J is the amount of set-back, and the amount of material required for a bend is *A* plus *B* minus *J*.

As an example of how to use the "J" chart, let us assume that our metal has a thickness of .050 and is to be bent on a radius of ⅛ inch through a closed angle (or bevel) of 15 degrees. First place a straight edge across the chart, connecting the .050 thickness figure with the ⅛ inch radius figure. Then follow the line of 15 degrees (closed bevel) to its intersection with the straight edge and the curved line #.19. The *J* dimension nearest the intersection denotes the required set-back.

Set-back is subtracted only once for each bend. *A* or *B* minus ½ *J* indicates the distance from the center of the bend to the end of the metal.

The method of determining radius, previously mentioned in discussing the empirical formula, may also apply when using the "J" chart. However, this method is sometimes highly inaccurate and should be used only when definite radius figures are not furnished by the plant.

Almost every old-time aircraft mechanic has his own way of figuring bending allowances—some of them amazingly accurate. One of these is the combined "Set-Back and Bend-Allowance Chart" (Figure 52). But the beginner who lacks experience with various materials will

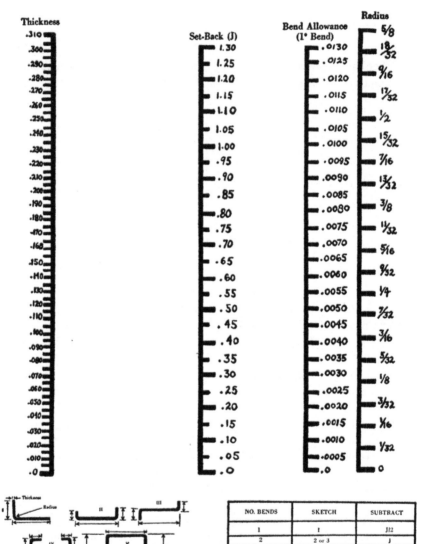

NO. BENDS	SKETCH	SUBTRACT
1	1	J|2
2	2 or 3	J
4	4 or 5	2J

To Find Developed Width of Sections Shown:

1. Put a straight edge over the appropriate thickness and radius scales, and find the set-back.

2. Find the total over-all dimensions of the section.

3. Subtract from the latter as in box above.

FIG. 52. SET-BACK AND BEND-ALLOWANCE CHART

learn more by sticking to the empirical formula or the "J" chart in his initial calculations.

Aircraft Tubing and Fittings

Seamless .tubing and appropriate fittings are used in all parts of modern airplanes to protect control cables, as fuel and oil lines, for instrument connections, and so forth. This is commonly termed "aircraft plumbing."

The types of tubing ordinarily used are aluminum alloy (2S and 52S), stainless steel, and copper.

Tubing may be cut to the required size with either a special cutting tool or an ordinary hacksaw. The only requirement here is to make sure that the cut is even and square. Then the ends of the tube should be filed and burred—so they will be smooth and provide a good close fit.

There are several designs for tube-bending tools, all comparatively easy to understand and use. Each includes a mandrel which slips inside the tube to govern its shape, and the real technique of operating any bender consists of knowing how to apply the mandrel. This technique is illustrated in Figure 53.

Fittings required to connect tubing at the various stations throughout an airplane are numerous, their types depending entirely upon the purpose for which they are respectively used. Some of the more popular types are listed in Figure 54.

Flaring

In order to make various types of fittings, or to secure a satisfactory outlet, as in an exhaust pipe, it is sometimes necessary to "flare" tubing. This is a method of making the lips of a tube end spread out as shown in Figure 55.

Flaring may be accomplished by hand tools, but in modern factories a "spinning" machine does the job.

Prior to the flaring operation, the tubing must be cleaned thoroughly in order to prevent impregnation of dirt particles in the flare. Alu-

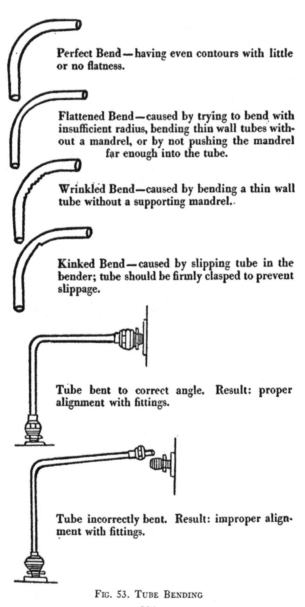

Perfect Bend — having even contours with little or no flatness.

Flattened Bend — caused by trying to bend with insufficient radius, bending thin wall tubes without a mandrel, or by not pushing the mandrel far enough into the tube.

Wrinkled Bend — caused by bending a thin wall tube without a supporting mandrel.

Kinked Bend — caused by slipping tube in the bender; tube should be firmly clasped to prevent slippage.

Tube bent to correct angle. Result: proper alignment with fittings.

Tube incorrectly bent. Result: improper alignment with fittings.

Fig. 53. Tube Bending

114

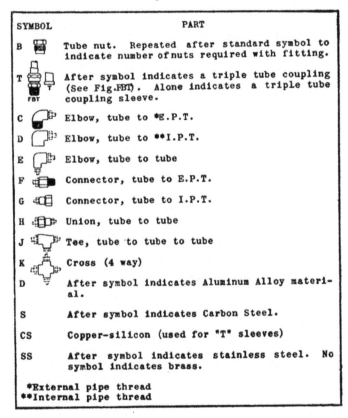

SYMBOL		PART
B		Tube nut. Repeated after standard symbol to indicate number of nuts required with fitting.
T		After symbol indicates a triple tube coupling (See Fig.FBT). Alone indicates a triple tube coupling sleeve.
C		Elbow, tube to *E.P.T.
D		Elbow, tube to **I.P.T.
E		Elbow, tube to tube
F		Connector, tube to E.P.T.
G		Connector, tube to I.P.T.
H		Union, tube to tube
J		Tee, tube to tube to tube
K		Cross (4 way)
D		After symbol indicates Aluminum Alloy material.
S		After symbol indicates Carbon Steel.
CS		Copper-silicon (used for "T" sleeves)
SS		After symbol indicates stainless steel. No symbol indicates brass.

*External pipe thread
**Internal pipe thread

Fig. 54. Types of Aircraft Fittings

minum alloy tubing can be flared by cold-working, but steel tubing must first be heated.

A steel band, fastened around the tubing, limits the length of the flare. The wall thickness of the flared tube ends should not be less than 85 per cent of the wall thickness of the tube proper.

The flaring with hand tools is usually accomplished with a steel die, forced into the end of the tube (see Figure 56).

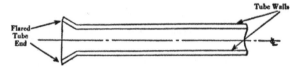

FIG. 55. TUBE FLARING

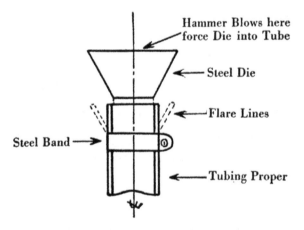

FIG. 56. USE OF STEEL DIE TO FLARE TUBING

Torque Wrenches

Unfamiliar to mechanics in many industries, the torque wrench is a comparatively recent development that is of especial interest and importance to aircraft workers.

The word "torque" indicates the power or force that is required for a circular motion. Hence, a torque wrench is a wrench with a gage which indicates the amount of pressure being exerted in the movements of tightening a bolt, turnbuckle, pipe fitting, and so forth.

Torque wrenches are of especial importance to the aircraft mechanic because they enable him to avoid excessive tightening, which stretches and distorts threaded parts—eventually causing failures.

They record "torque moment" in terms of "PSI" (pounds per square inch).

In applying torque loads, an effort should be made to stop within the minimum limits, so that further pressure can be exerted to align cotter pin holes, etc., without exceeding the maximum limits. A nut should never be turned back for such alignment.

The following table indicates the torque moment for the commonly-used steel aircraft bolts with a tensile strength of 125,000 PSI:

TORQUE

Bolt Size	Inch Lbs.	Ft. Lbs.
$\frac{3}{16}$	35 to 50	3 to 4
$\frac{1}{4}$	55 to 90	5 to 7
$\frac{5}{16}$	90 to 150	8 to 12
$\frac{3}{8}$	200 to 350	17 to 29
$\frac{7}{16}$	350 to 600	30 to 50
$\frac{1}{2}$	500 to 850	42 to 70
$\frac{5}{8}$	850 to 1300	71 to 108
$\frac{3}{4}$	1200 to 1750	100 to 146

The above figures apply only when standard steel nuts are used without lubrication. If the threads are lubricated, the torque moment should be reduced 30 per cent.

Aircraft bolts of the 24ST aluminum alloy type should be tightened in accordance with the table below:

TORQUE

Bolt Size	Inch Lbs.	Ft. Lbs.
$\frac{3}{16}$ (No. 10)	10 to 14	
$\frac{1}{4}$	20 to 35	2 to 3
$\frac{5}{16}$	50 to 75	4 to 6
$\frac{3}{8}$	80 to 110	7 to 9
$\frac{7}{16}$	100 to 140	9 to 11
$\frac{5}{8}$	400 to 460	24 to 38

The above torques apply even when anti-sieze paste is used. Anti-sieze paste is zinc dust and petroleum jelly.

Socket Wrenches

Because they are adapted to so many different types of work, socket wrenches are generally preferred in making routine aircraft installations. The average socket-wrench set includes four handles (known as the "T," ratchet, flex, and "spintite" types) and an indefinite number of sockets, designed to fit over nuts of various sizes and types. Any one of the handles will fit any one of the sockets, depending upon which happens to be most convenient for a particular job.

Since socket wrenches are used almost exclusively for tightening nuts and bolts, the main thing an aircraft worker should remember regarding their use is to select a socket the correct size for each individual job. Undersized sockets naturally cannot be used, but oversized sockets will mutilate the nut or bolt head. Also, the sockets should be carefully polished and be free from burrs.

Screwdrivers

A screwdriver in aircraft work is the same as a screwdriver in any other type of mechanical work—its purpose being to tighten screws, clevis bolts, and other small parts. It should be kept sharp, but never used as a chisel or pry.

The only really unusual screwdriver used in aircraft work is the one designed to fit "Reed and Prince" and "Phillips" head screws (which,

Special Screwdriver

FIG. 57. SCREWDRIVER FOR USE WITH REED & PRINCE AND
PHILLIPS HEAD SCREWS

Phillips   Reed and Prince
Screw Head   Screw Head

FIG. 58. SPECIAL SCREWS

incidentally, aren't covered by government specifications). This screw-driver and the appropriate screws are of particular value when working over thin skin—where a slip could cause considerable damage to surrounding material. The drawings in Figures 57 and 58 show why this is so.

Taps and Dies

Sometimes it is necessary to cut threads into various types of materials in order to apply a screw or bolt, and the tool used for this work is called a tap. Taps are made in all sizes, and can match any type of screw or bolt threads. The average tap looks something like a screw with four "flutes" down its sides to remove small chips of metal. A "starting" tap must be used first in threading the material; it has a tapered end which facilitates the starting operation. Next a "plug" tap, with only a slight taper (two or three threads) is used; then the job is finished with a "bottoming" tap, which is shaped so as to make a full set of threads at the bottom of the hole. The three kinds of taps are shown in Figure 59.

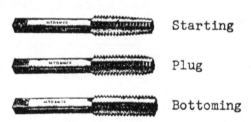

Starting

Plug

Bottoming

FIG. 59. TAPS

When using a tap, it is best to back the tap up every quarter turn to clear the chips. The axis of the tap and the axis of the hole should form a straight line. A tap that is started crooked must be removed from the material and started again.

In the business of cutting threads, the antithesis of the tap is the "thread die," which is usually as pictured in Figure 60.

Thread dies are used for the job of putting threads on various types of special bolts and so forth. A thread die is tapered to facilitate starting on one side, while the other side is sized so as to provide the correct

FIG. 60. THREAD DIE

thread depth. On most dies there is an adjustment (set screw) for sizing. Otherwise, the procedure of die cutting threads is much the same as tapping.

Both taps and dies are known by the sizes of the threads they are designed to cut.

Files

The names of files depend largely upon the type of work for which they were designed—such as hand file, flat file, mill file, knife file, etc. File nomenclature is shown in Figure 61.

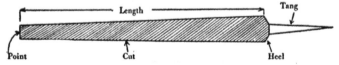

FIG. 61. FILE NOMENCLATURE

The "tang" is shaped so as to grip a wooden handle; it is not included in measurements showing file lengths.

The three principal file cuts are called single, double, and vixen. The single-cut file has single rows of teeth extending across its face at an angle of about 65 or 85 degrees; coarse-grade files of this type often are called "floats." The double-cut file has teeth in rows of about 45- and 80-degree angles and crossing one another; the angles vary somewhat, depending upon the type of work for which the individual

file is designed. Vixen files have curved rows of teeth in three classes—
regular, fine, and smooth.

Files are graded according to the coarseness or fineness of their cuts
—the most important grades being rough, coarse, bastard, second
cut, smooth, and dead smooth.

The vixen-type file is designed for rapid filing on soft metals and
wood; it leaves a very smooth finish. All regular-cut files are suitable

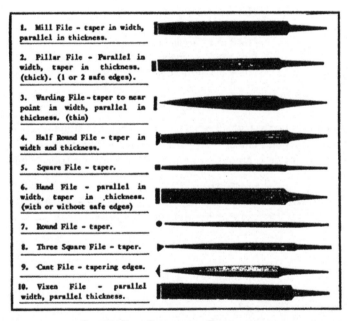

1. Mill File - taper in width, parallel in thickness.

2. Pillar File - Parallel in width, taper in thickness. (thick). (1 or 2 safe edges).

3. Warding File - taper to near point in width, parallel in thickness. (thin)

4. Half Round File - taper in width and thickness.

5. Square File - taper.

6. Hand File - parallel in width, taper in thickness. (with or without safe edges)

7. Round File - taper.

8. Three Square File - taper.

9. Cant File - tapering edges.

10. Vixen File - parallel width, parallel thickness.

FIG. 62. FILE SHAPES AND DESIGNATIONS

for rough work on cast iron, soft steel, copper, brass, aluminum, and
so forth. Fine-cut files are generally used on harder metals, while
smooth-cut files are best where little material is to be removed and a
good finish is desired.

File shapes and their appropriate designations are shown in Figure 62.

Files are essentially cutting tools, and should be handled with great care. All filing should be done in the cutting direction. Both the file and the work upon which it is used should be thoroughly clean. Most files can be cleaned on a "file card"—that is, a brush with the fine wire bristles and a small sharp pick in its handle.

Files are numbered according to the grades of their various cuts, in the following manner:

> No. 000—coarse cut
> No. 00—bastard cut
> No. 0 to 1—second cuts
> No. 2 and 3—smooth cuts
> No. 4 and 5—dead smooth cuts

Joggling

When it is necessary to keep a smooth surface in splicing skin over a framework joint, one or more of the component parts must be "joggled." The joggle is an offset of one of the pieces in a splice sufficient

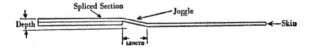

FIG. 63. A JOGGLE

to allow a smooth surface over a joint. Joggles in aluminum alloy shapes should be at least three times as long as they are deep. For an example, see Figure 63.

7

ASSEMBLY

In aircraft work it is sometimes difficult to determine where parts construction ends and assembly begins; while the duties of each department in any factory may seem clearly defined, all branches are so closely interwoven that one unit may at any time be called upon to assume the duties of another unit. For example, final-assembly workers are sometimes obliged to make their own small parts; simultaneously, parts men may be erecting various assemblies.

However, as explained in Chapter 1, assembly operations in most factories come under two general headings—primary and final. Primary assembly includes the construction of major parts—wing sections, tail sections, fuselage sections, and so forth—and final assembly is where these major parts are incorporated in the form of a finished airplane.

The first step in assembling an airplane, or a major part, is to get a suitable set of "jigs and fixtures" which will hold the necessary materials in place while they are made into a single unit. The construction of jigs and fixtures is a "parts and processes" job, but their use is confined largely to the assembly departments.

Bolts, screws, and so forth are used in a number of assembly operations; but the most important methods of uniting various structural parts are welding and riveting. At present riveting is considered the foremost assembly technique, though welding has in many respects proved itself to be a superior process.

The chief advantage of riveting is its simplicity; a man can learn the fundamentals of this technique in the course of a few hours— becoming proficient at it after a few days' practice. On the other hand, a good welder must study and practice for months before he can be considered reasonably accomplished and capable of passing the rigid government qualification tests.

Both welding and riveting will be discussed with more detail later in this chapter.

Jigs and Fixtures

A "jig" is a frame or body to which work may be fastened with "fixtures" in order to facilitate the construction of well-made units. Besides holding the work in a suitable position, it may include a device which will guide the workman's tools—so that both the work and the tool are located in the true position relative to one another.

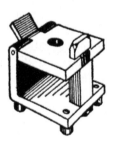 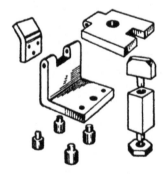

Fig. 64. Built-up Jig   Fig. 65. Jig Parts

The *built-up* jig is usually applied only to small parts, such as battery supports and gear boxes. It is typified in the drawings of Figures 64 and 65.

The *cast* type jig is usually most common in all types of engineering work. Though sometimes rather complicated, it is always produced as a single unit. (See Figure 66.)

Welded jigs are becoming especially popular in aircraft work, because they are so useful in handling large assemblies. Typical of welded jigs is the "move" jig, shown in the accompanying photo of a final-assembly line.

Above. The "mating" jig is being used with this Hudson bomber. A frame support, it holds up the center section of the wing to the underside of the fuselage. (*Lockheed Aircraft Corp. Photo*)

Below. Secured in "move" jigs, Ryan trainer fuselage sections are ready for action on a moving final-assembly line. (*Ryan Aeronautical Co. Photo*)

Carriages support these A-20 Havoc attack bombers on the moving final-assembly line. (*Douglas Aircraft Co. Photo*)

FIG. 66. CAST TYPE JIG

Big *wooden* jigs are sometimes used in constructing seaplanes and flying boats. They are heavily padded with canvas and their purpose is to support a hull without damaging the keel.

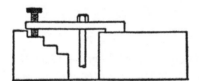

FIG. 67. SCREW-ADJUSTED CLAMP AND PACK-ING BLOCK

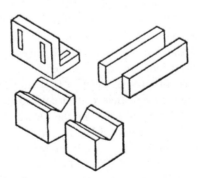

FIG. 68. ANGLE PLATE (ABOVE LEFT), PARALLEL BLOCKS (RIGHT), "V" BLOCKS (BELOW)

Numerous types of *fixtures* are used in aircraft work; they include blocks, clamping devices, angle plates, and so forth. Their purpose is virtually the same as that of a jig, but they are far more numerous and

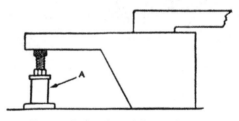

FIG. 69. SCREW JACK (*A*) AND BLOCK

far more often used. Some of the more ordinary fixtures are shown in Figures 67, 68, and 69.

Riveting

Riveting is a method of joining together two or more pieces of metal with a rivet. Generally a rivet is of the same material as the pieces of metal it unites, and its appearance before the riveting operation resembles that of a threadless screw or bolt.

Most of the rivets used in aircraft work are covered by AN specifications. Their main characteristics are shown in Figure 70.

The rivets shown here are all aluminum and aluminum alloy types, their exact compositions being in conformity with their head markings. A dimpled head indicates dural, annealed (A17ST). The head with a tit designates an "ice-box rivet"—that is, a dural rivet which must be heat-treated, frozen, then driven cold (17S). An unmarked head indicates pure aluminum (2S). Dashes on the head identify another type of dural ice-box rivet (either 17S or 24S).

Dural rivets are used on virtually all aircraft structural parts, the 17S ice-box type being preferred. Pure aluminum rivets are most popular in gas tanks, conduit boxes, and so forth, where stresses are slight.

The simplest form of riveting is accomplished with a hammer and

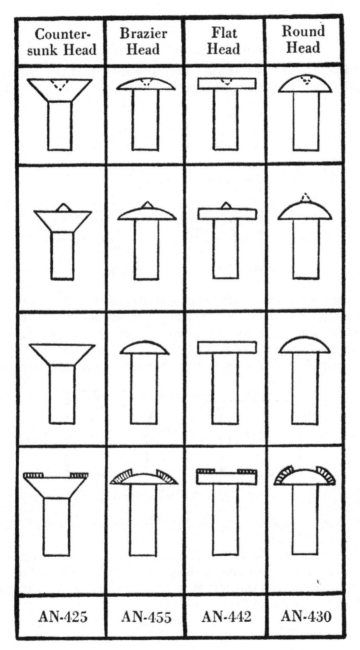

Counter-sunk Head	Brazier Head	Flat Head	Round Head
AN-425	AN-455	AN-442	AN-430

FIG. 70. RIVET CHARACTERISTICS

bucking bar. The bucking bar is a smooth piece of hardened steel, and during the operation it is held against the rivet as shown in Figure 71.

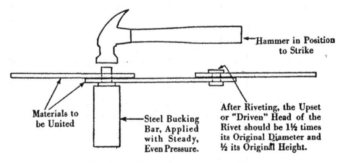

Hammer in Position
to Strike

Materials to
be United

Steel Bucking
Bar, Applied
with Steady,
Even Pressure.

After Riveting, the Upset
or "Driven" Head of the
Rivet should be 1½ times
its Original Diameter and
½ its Original Height.

FIG. 71. HAMMER AND BUCKING BAR

The most important thing to remember in selecting rivets is to get the proper size. To do this, it is necessary to know how rivets are dimensioned. The length of all except countersunk rivets is measured from the base of the head to the tip of the shank. The length of a countersunk rivet is measured from the top of the head to the tip of

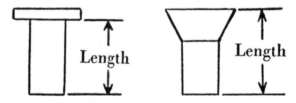

Length

Length

FIG. 72. RIVET MEASUREMENT

the shank. This measurement is illustrated in Figure 72; the countersunk rivet is on the right.

The extension of a rivet is that part of the shank which extends beyond the head and grip on the other side of the material to be riveted. The grip is that part of the shank which is enclosed by the material. (See Figure 73.)

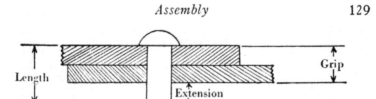

FIG. 73. EXTENSION AND GRIP OF RIVET

The spacing of a rivet should be not less than three times its diameter from adjoining rivets, and not more than twenty-four times the thickness of the material being riveted. In dealing with sheet metal, no rivet should be placed closer than twice its diameter to the edge of the material. When the material is a nonferrous casting, the rivet should be three times its diameter from the edge. Generally the correct spacings of all rivets are noted on blueprints. However, when this is lacking, the "Rivet-Spacing Chart" on page 130 will be found convenient.

When the correct spacing has been determined, holes must be drilled through the adjacent materials for the rivets. This is usually accomplished with an electric drill motor, using drills as follows:

DRILL SIZE	RIVET DIAMETER
#51	$\frac{1}{16}''$
#40	$\frac{3}{32}''$
#30	$\frac{1}{8}''$
#21	$\frac{5}{32}''$
#11	$\frac{3}{16}''$
$\frac{1}{4}$	$\frac{1}{4}''$

The metal scribe should never be used for laying out holes on sheet metal; it will scratch the material and eventually cause corrosion. A plain, soft lead pencil does the job most satisfactorily.

Two machines are used for drilling—the drill press and the portable hand motor. Drill presses are shown in an accompanying photo. The hand motor looks something like a bulky automatic pistol, and is operated electrically—simply by pressing a trigger.

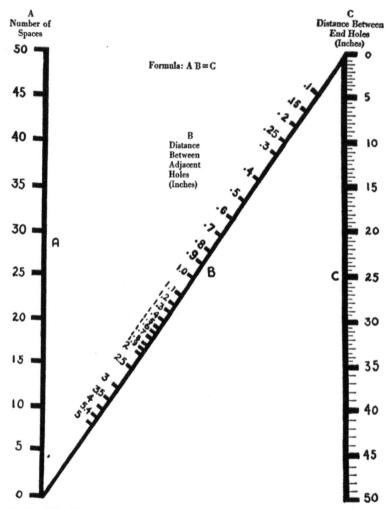

A
Number of
Spaces

C
Distance Between
End Holes
(Inches)

Formula: A B = C

B
Distance
Between
Adjacent
Holes
(Inches)

To Use This Chart:

1. Determine number of spaces (or rivets) required.
2. Determine inches of distance between end holes.
3. Place straight edge so as to connect appropriate figures in vertical lines on chart.
4. Find inches distance between adjacent holes at point where straight edge intersects diagonal line in chart.

FIG. 74. RIVET-SPACING CHART

In any type of drilling, the drill operator should be careful not to apply too much pressure. Excessive pressure causes the drill to plunge through the metal too fast, forming large burrs around the lower edges of the hole. Burrs must be removed by hand with a ream, or over-sized drill, before rivets can be inserted in the hole—and the result is a considerable waste of time.

The drill should always be held perpendicular to the material. At any other angle, it will make an enlarged hole and the rivet will not fit properly.

High-speed drilling is necessary when working on aluminum or its alloys; low speeds are best for iron or steel.

A bad rivet can be removed by drilling a hole through its head to the tip of the shank. If the shank is drilled too deep, however, the original hole in the material will be enlarged and further repair work will be necessary. The drilled head can be knocked off with a hammer and chisel, and the shank can be ejected with a punch.

Squeeze riveting is preferred, when practicable, in aircraft work; it is the simplest, easiest, and most efficient of all riveting methods. Either a portable or standard squeezer may be used; both machines operate

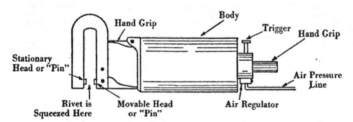

FIG. 75. PORTABLE SQUEEZER

on the same principle and get their power from compressed air. The portable squeezer is usually built along the lines shown in Figure 75.

The standard squeezer is usually larger than the portable type and cannot be carried about from job to job because it has a stationary base. One man can operate either of these squeezers.

Besides being fast and easy, squeeze riveting is preferred because it eliminates excessive work-hardening of rivet metals. The squeezer installs a rivet in a single operation, and can be gaged so as to form a perfect head each time it is used. "Pin" sets of various types enable the squeezer to fit any "manufactured" rivet head.

The main thing to remember in using a squeezer is to get the air pressure adjusted properly. It is best to start off at a low pressure and

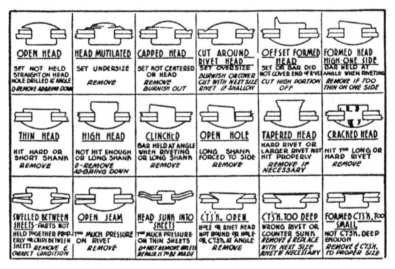

FIG. 76. CAUSES FOR RIVET REJECTION
(Courtesy of Consolidated Aircraft Corp.)

increase it gradually until the driven head of the first rivet has been perfectly formed. After that, finishing a job is just a matter of pressing the trigger.

Gun riveting is more popular than squeeze riveting in aircraft work because it can be used in so many different ways—and in spots that would be inaccessible to the squeezer.

The three types of riveting guns in general use are called the "vibrator," the "slow hitter," and the "one shot." All are operated by compressed air.

The vibrator gun hits fast, light blows and is usually best for small

Above. Drill presses are used whenever possible in aircraft work. Their perpendicular setting makes it impossible to drill enlarged holes.
(*Consolidated Aircraft Corp. Photo*)

Below. Driving a rivet in the fuselage of a bomber. The shape of the driven head on the rivet depends largely upon the straightness of the line between the rivet gun (left) and the bucking bar (right). (*Consolidated Photo*)

Riveting a light wing rib by means of a standard or stationary squeezer. Note the "fixtures" which hold the rib parts in place. (*Piper Aircraft Corp. Photo*)

rivets ($\frac{3}{32}''$ to $\frac{1}{8}''$ diameter). It is comparatively easy to use, but its numerous blows tend to work-harden rivets to a state of extreme brittleness.

The slow-hitter gun is more widely used because it will drive $\frac{3}{32}''$ to $\frac{3}{16}''$ rivets in less time and without excessive work-hardening. Its blows are slow and hard.

In riveting with either the slow hitter or vibrator, the rivet gun is placed on the manufactured rivet head while the driven head is formed on a steel bucking bar. But when the one-shot gun is used, this procedure is reversed. The bucking bar has a special "groove" to fit the manufactured head, and the gun forms the driven head with a single hard blow.

Two workers are required in gun riveting. One handles the gun, while the other manipulates the bucking bar.

Good gun riveting necessitates considerably more practice than other riveting processes, but it can be readily mastered by most people with mechanical inclinations.

Since rivet guns are used often in attaching sheet metal to fuselage and wing sections, the main thing a workman must avoid is the "oil can." Briefly, the oil can is a wrinkle in sheet metal, caused by improper drilling and fitting of skin. It can be detected by merely pressing on the surface of the riveted sheet metal—to see whether it snaps, like the bottom of a regular oil can.

Countersunk riveting is often favored in exterior work, because the countersunk head does not produce "drag" like other rivet heads. The two kinds of countersunk rivets in general use are those with "head angles" of 78 and 115 degrees, respectively. Special "countersink" drills must be used in making holes for these rivets, and extra care must be taken in order to avoid cutting wider than the diameter of the rivet head.

The bucking bar is usually placed on the manufactured head of the countersunk rivet, and the one-shot rivet gun is considered best for making the driven head.

Counterpressing, or "flush riveting," is sometimes used as a substitute for regular countersunk riveting—especially when working with skin that is not thick enough to withstand countersink drilling. It is faster than countersinking, but is not generally preferred by engineering experts because it is not conducive to great structural strength.

Ordinary countersunk rivets are used in counterpressing, those with 115-degree heads being most popular. A straight hole is drilled in the material, and a "dimpling" set is placed in a standard or portable

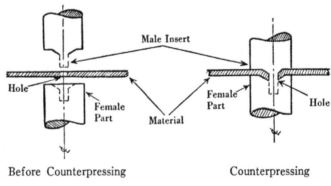

Before Counterpressing   Counterpressing

Fig. 77. Use of "Dimpling" Set

squeezer. This set has a male insert which is shaped like the rivet's head, and a female part which is shaped like the rivet hole. Hence, the material is counterpressed as shown in Figure 77.

When the counterpressing is finished, the rivet is inserted in the hole and its second head driven. Figure 78 shows the difference between countersunk and counterpressed rivets.

Fig. 78A. Countersunk Rivet Fig. 78B. Counterpressed Rivet

Welding

According to the American Welding Society, welding is "the localized intimate union of metal parts in the plastic, or plastic and molten states with the application of mechanical pressure or blows, and in the molten states without the application of mechanical pressure or blows."

Gas welding and *arc* (*or electric*) *welding* are the most popular types in the American aircraft industry at present. However, three additional types of welding have been developed and seem destined to become of vast importance to the industry of the future.

The first of the new types is *"atomic hydrogen"* welding, developed by the Ryan Aeronautical Company. This so-called atomic welding has already been included in United States Army aircraft specifications, although most factories have not yet had a chance to experiment with the process. It is similar, in practice, to electric welding; its efficiency is a result of the tremendous heat caused by the breaking down of atoms.

"Heliarc welding" is another new process that is similar to regular electric welding. Developed by the Northrup Aircraft factory, it has made possible the welding of magnesium. Noninflammable helium gas is the secret in this instance. Ejected from an electric welding torch, the helium envelops the molten material that is to be welded and prevents oxidization. Heliarc welding has been used with surprising success on iron, steel, and other metals, as well as magnesium.

"Zero welding" is a new development of the Ford aircraft plant at Willow Run, Michigan. Ford engineers describe this kind of welding as "the creating of a frigid area and shooting a hot current through it." The result is increased efficiency in making "spot welds," a process which will be described later in this chapter.

The elemental principle of all welding is seen in a simple operation performed by a blacksmith over his anvil; it consists of heating two pieces of wrought iron or steel to a white heat and hammering them together. In good work of this kind, it is impossible to see the joint; but, if the joint were tested, it would show only about 75 per cent of the strength of the original metal.

In modern aircraft work, where the most exacting of requirements prevail, it is often found that welded sections are actually

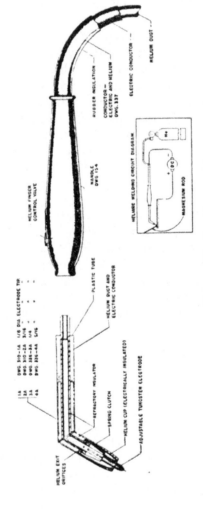

HELIARC WELDING TORCH

(Northrop Aircraft, Inc. Photo)

stronger than the original metal; tests on "pulling machines" show that a good weld will hold its shape without breaking longer than will the pieces of metal it unites.

Resistance welding is probably the simplest form of aircraft welding. This is electric welding, done in machines. It is applicable to light work, sometimes a substitute for riveting, and is classified as butt, flash, spot, and seam welding. A very heavy current at low voltage is passed through the parts to be welded; electrical resistance at the point of contact is high, causing the temperature of the parts to increase rapidly. Then mechanical pressure is applied to join the metal into a sound weld.

The two types of butt-resistance welding are called "slow butt welding" and "flash welding." In the slow process the heated parts are forced together, causing an upset at the weld. In the flash process the parts are brought together with only a slight pressure; arcing

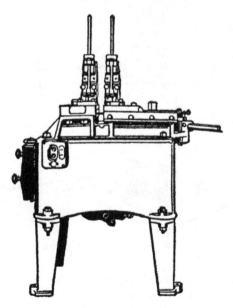

Fig. 79. Butt-Welding Machine

takes place and any unevenness at the ends burns away while the whole area of the ends is rapidly raised to a high temperature. Then suddenly heavy pressure is applied, and burnt metal is forced out in the form of a thin fin, leaving only sound metal in the weld proper. Slow butt welding is usually best on heavy materials, while flash welding is most suitable for thin sections—such as skin.

"Spot welding" is also good on light work; it is used extensively as a substitute for riveting. In this process, the materials are both heated and welded under pressure. Automatic machines make this just a simple matter of pulling levers, insofar as the operator is concerned.

Some typical welding machines are shown in Figures 79 and 80.

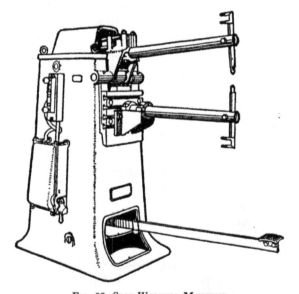

FIG. 80. SPOT-WELDING MACHINE

"Seam welding" (sometimes called "line welding") is a substitute method of spot welding, used on various water or liquid tight joints. Copper disc electrodes are used in this process.

Arc welding technically is electric welding without a machine, though grammatically all electric welding might be indicated by this heading. The two classes of arc welding are "metallic arc" and "carbon arc"; either class is effective on both alternating and direct electrical currents.

Fusion in arc welding is the result of an intentional "short circuit," which produces the required heat. This short circuit occurs when the

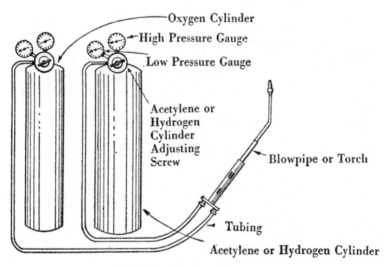

FIG. 81. GAS-WELDING EQUIPMENT

material to be welded intercepts an electric current traveling from a positive to a negative arc.

The essentials of a good weld are twofold. First, the surfaces to be united must be thoroughly fused and intimately mixed. Secondly, slag and oxide must be eliminated. Slag includes virtually all the burnt metal and other impurities that result from the welding process; oxide is an element of the air, which has a way of getting into molten metals and causing them to corrode.

Slag and oxide are eliminated in arc welding by the use of a

OXY-ACETYLENE FLAMES

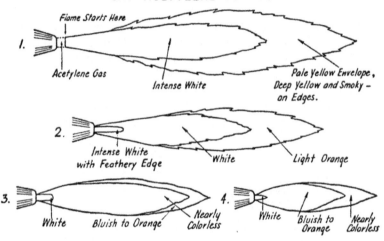

OXY-HYDROGEN FLAMES

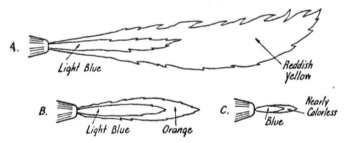

1. ACETYLENE FLAME—large, intensely white, smoky at outer end, obtained when first lighting torch.

2. CARBONIZING FLAME—can be easily recognized by the feathery edge of the white cone.

3. NEUTRAL FLAME—one clear, well-defined white cone surrounded by a nearly colorless flame of large volume.

4. OXIDIZING FLAME—can be recognized by its shorter envelope of flame and the small pointed white cone.

SKETCHES A, B, and C are respectively the reducing, neutral, and oxidizing oxy-hydrogen flames.

FIG. 82. WELDING FLAMES
(Courtesy of Aluminum Co. of America)

"flux" and the formation of a "gaseous shield." The flux fills in the weld and eliminates slag impurities; the gaseous shield keeps oxygen in the air from impregnating the molten metal.

Gas welding is currently the most common of aircraft welding processes, though its inferiority in view of recent developments in this field is recognized. It is a comparatively inexpensive process and is especially effective in working with aluminum.

Most gas welding is accomplished with an acetylene torch. The gas in this case is actually acetylene mixed with oxygen (see Glossary). Equipment for this work is shown in Figure 81.

In welding aluminum, oxygen and hydrogen are sometimes employed in place of oxygen and acetylene. However, the basic process remains unchanged.

The tank regulators, shown in the illustration of gas-welding equipment, control the pressure of the gases; regulators on the torch determine the quality of the welding flame. Some of the more common welding flames are shown in Figure 82.

The torch itself acts mainly as a mixer for the gases. A typical welding torch is shown in Figure 83.

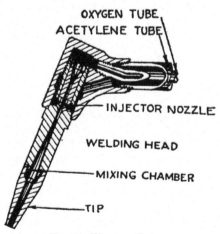

OXYGEN TUBE

ACETYLENE TUBE

INJECTOR NOZZLE

WELDING HEAD

MIXING CHAMBER

TIP

FIG. 83. WELDING TORCH

A "welding rod" is generally used in gas welding to help unite the materials in question, and the way this rod is used determines the type of welding. The three main types of gas welding are "forward," "backward," and "vertical."

In forward welding the blowpipe is preceded by the welding rod along the direction of the seam, both being held in the same vertical plane and approximately at right angles to one another. In backward welding the torch points in the direction of the completed weld and moves in the direction of the weld without lateral motion; meanwhile, the welding rod points in the opposite direction and is given a progressive circular movement. Vertical welding is virtually the same as forward welding, the chief difference being the fact that the material is held at a different angle. The differences between forward and backward types of welding are shown in Figure 84.

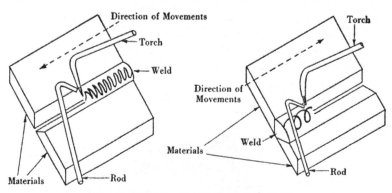

FIG. 84. FORWARD AND BACKWARD WELDING

The flux used in gas welding usually comes in the form of a paste. The welding rod is dipped in this paste prior to welding, so that both the rod and flux can be melted into the weld simultaneously.

Welding aluminum is one of the most important processes in aircraft production. Although it is a comparatively recent achievement, this is not a difficult job if the proper equipment is used.

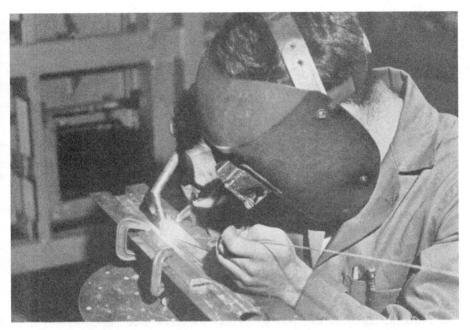

Above. Welding magnesium by the heliarc process. (*Northrop Aviation, Inc. Photo*)

Below. Zero welding on a new-type machine designed by engineers of the Ford Motor Company. Note the ice-covered "points." (*Ford Motor Co. Photo*)

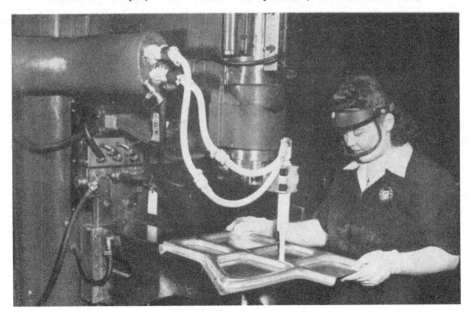

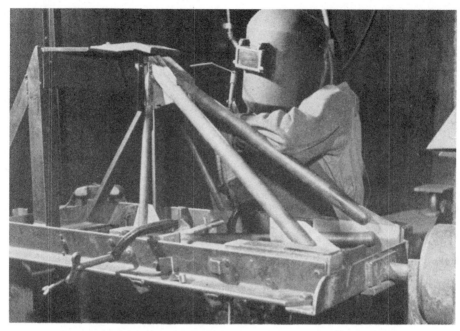

Above. Arc welding an airplane engine mount. Note the jigs and fixtures employed. (*Consolidated Aircraft Corp. Photo*)

Below. Gas welding an exhaust manifold section. (*Ryan Aeronautical Co. Photo*)

The main reason aluminum cannot be welded like other metals is the fact that it does not change color with the application of heat. This makes it difficult to determine when the material is hot enough without reaching the liquid stage. Also, hot aluminum has a strong tendency to form oxides.

A neutral hydrogen flame is generally considered best for welding aluminum and its alloys. However, acetylene and electrical welding methods may also be employed successfully.

Torch tips for gas welding may be selected in accordance with the following table:

	OXY-HYDROGEN				OXY-ACETYLENE		
Metal Thickness B & S Gauge	Diam. of Orifice in Tip Inch	Oxygen Pressure Lb./sq. in.	Hydrogen Pressure Lb./sq. in.		Diam. of Orifice in Tip Inch	Oxygen Pressure Lb./sq. in.	Acetylene Pressure Lb./sq. in.
24–22	0.035	1	1		0.025	1	1
20–18	0.045	1	1		0.035	1	1
16–14	0.065	2	1		0.055	2	2
12–10	0.075	2	1		0.065	3	3
⅛–³⁄₁₆	0.095	3	2		0.075	4	4
¼	0.105	4	2		0.085	5	5
⁵⁄₁₆	0.115	4	2		0.085	5	5
⅜	0.125	5	3		0.095	6	6
⅝	0.150	8	6		0.105	7	7

Courtesy of Aluminum Co. of America

There are several excellent types of flux that may be used in welding aluminum. They are usually sold in a powder form and can be made into the required paste by simply adding water. Flux is especially important in welding aluminum, since its purpose is to eliminate the previously mentioned oxides.

The Aluminum Company of America (Alcoa) provides the following information regarding the wire or rod used in welding aluminum:

The unheat-treatable aluminum alloys Alcoa 2S and 3S should ordinarily be welded with 2S wire, but the unheat-treatable alloy 52S and the heat-treatable alloys (51S and 53S) should ordinarily be welded with a rod consisting of 5% silicon and 95% aluminum (43S alloy).

On jobs where the parts are held tightly in jigs, 43S welding wire should be used, regardless of the composition of the alloy. This is more necessary, however, for the strong alloys as they are more hot short than pure aluminum. Alcoa 43S welding wire fuses readily with all aluminum alloys, has good corrosion resistance and high strength. It is satisfactory to use in welding any of the ordinary aluminum alloys.

The 43S welding wire has a relatively slight solidification contraction. Because of its lower melting point and wider melting range it remains molten, or at least soft for a longer time than the base metal, and fills in the voids caused by the solidification shrinkage of the welded parts in the same way that a gate fills in the shrinkage of a casting. This welding wire is noteworthy for its freedom from hot shortness. It has fair ductility and strength at temperatures just under the melting point. It will, therefore, readily stand the strains incidental to welding.

Welding rod sizes have been standardized at $\frac{1}{16}''$, $\frac{1}{8}''$, $\frac{3}{16}''$ and $\frac{1}{4}''$ diameter. A rod diameter should be chosen that will approximate the thickness of the material to be welded. Ordinarily, $\frac{1}{8}$ inch diameter rod is suitable for welding any thickness of metal up to $\frac{1}{8}$ inch; and $\frac{3}{16}$ inch diameter rod for the heavier gauges. However, this welding rod may be obtained in any gauge to suit individual preference.

In working with aluminum sheet which is $\frac{3}{8}$ inch or more in thickness, or with the larger aluminum castings, a "preheating" process must precede welding. The entire surfaces of the parts to be united should be preheated to a temperature of between 700° and 800° F. in order to avoid heat strains and to reduce the amount of gas required to melt the seam. When light-gage aluminum is concerned, however, no heat is required beyond the bounds of the seam or spot to be welded.

The accompanying tables will be found valuable in welding aluminum electrically: [1]

[1] Courtesy Aluminum Company of America.

APPROXIMATE MACHINE SETTINGS FOR SEAM WELDING ALUMINUM ALLOYS

Alloy	Thickness Inch	Pressure Lb.	Cycles		Spots per inch	Approx. "On" RMS Amperes
			On	Off		
52S-½H	0.025	600	1	6½	18.0	26,000
52S-½H	0.032	680	1	6½	16.0	29,000
52S-½H	0.040	760	1	6½	14.3	32,000
52S-½H	0.051	855	1½	6	12.6	36,000
52S-½H	0.064	960	1½	6	11.3	37,500
52S-½H	0.072	1015	1½	6	10.6	39,000
52S-½H	0.081	1080	2	11½	10.0	40,000
52S-½H	0.102	1210	2	11½	9.0	42,500

For 52S-¼H—Reduce pressure 10%
For 52S-O —Reduce pressure 25%
For 3S-½H—Reduce pressure 25%

ELECTRODE SIZE AND MACHINE SETTING FOR ALUMINUM METALLIC-ARC WELDS

Thickness Inch	Electrode Diameter Inch	Amperes	Rods Per Pound
0.064	⅛	45–55	32
0.081	⅛	55–65	32
0.102	⅛	65–75	32
0.125	⅛	75–85	32
5⁄32	⅛ or 5⁄32	85–100	32–23
3⁄16	5⁄32	100–125	23
¼	5⁄32 or 3⁄16	125–175	23–17
5⁄16	3⁄16	175–225	17
3⁄8	¼	225–300	10.5

Persons with practical welding experience must pass government tests before they are eligible for work in an aircraft factory. Typical of these tests are the requirements of Army Air Forces specification

Aircraft Construction Handbook

MACHINE SETTINGS FOR SPOT WELDING ALUMINUM ALLOYS

Gauge		Time Cycles	Current Amperes	Electrode Pressure	
B & S No.	Inch			Min. Lb.	Max. Lb.
26	0.016	4	14,000	200	400
24	0.020	6	16,000	300	500
22	0.025	6	17,000	300	500
20	0.032	8	18,000	400	600
18	0.040	8	20,000	400	600
16	0.051	10	22,000	500	700
14	0.064	10	24,000	500	700
12	0.081	12	28,000	600	800
10	0.102	12	32,000	800	1000
8	0.128	15	35,000	800	1200

20013-B entitled "Welding Procedure for Certification of Welders." A complete copy of this welding specification may be obtained by writing the Chief, Material Division, U.S. Army Air Forces, Wright Field, Dayton, Ohio. In part, it reads as follows:

This specification covers the procedure for the examination and certification of welders assigned to the welding of aircraft, aircraft parts and accessories.

The welders shall be graded into the following classifications:

Oxy-acetylene Gas Welders, Classes A, A-1, and B.
Electric Arc Welders, Class A, A-1, and B.
Atomic Hydrogen Welders, Class A.
Oxy-hydrogen Welders, Class A.

A welder must pass the qualification tests for the class in which he is to be employed and must pass the qualification tests for each of the following groups of alloys that he will weld:

Group I. Plain carbon steel and alloy steels.
Group II. Stainless and corrosion resistant steels.
Group III. Nickel alloys.
Group IV. Aluminum alloys.
Group V. Magnesium alloys.

Oxy-acetylene Class A or A-1 welders who have passed the qualification tests for Group I alloys are not eligible to weld alloys in Groups II, III, IV, and V unless they qualify by welding an alloy in each group. A welder who has qualified by welding a given alloy is eligible to weld other alloys in the same group without taking another examination.

The following restrictions apply to welders who have been issued certificates:

Class A—Qualified to weld all airplane parts and accessories manufactured from the groups of alloys for which he is qualified.

Class A-1—Qualified to weld only airplane parts and accessories fabricated from tubing stock or combinations of tubing and sheet stock from the groups of alloys for which he has qualified.

Class B—Qualified to weld only Group I alloys which are used in the manufacture of low stressed accessories and airplane parts which are not part of the primary or secondary structure. This includes such parts as fairing brackets, steps, and supports for instruments and miscellaneous equipment.

Navy welding specifications are available at the Bureau of Aeronautics, Navy Department, Washington, D.C.

8

INSPECTION

The reputation of a manufacturer depends on the quality of his product, and the quality of his product is largely a matter of proper inspection. For no matter how good a workman may be, he is never the best judge of his own work.

Inspection is of particular importance in the aircraft industry, because human lives are at stake as well as the manufacturer's reputation. In some branches of manufacturing, weight and close attention to limits, tolerances, and details are not so important; but in aviation they are vitally necessary. A number of fundamentally excellent airplanes have been seriously handicapped or damaged due to neglect of relatively small details.

Most aircraft workers think of an inspector as a sort of supercritic, with the power of life or death over their work. But the inspector's job is not just a matter of finding flaws. No piece of engineering work can be absolutely perfect, and a man of sufficient experience can find discrepancies in almost any item that comes to his attention. Therefore, the value or ability of an inspector is not measured by the number of rejections he makes; it is, rather, indicated by his ability to determine whether an article may be used—even though it may not be in absolute conformity with drawings, specifications, or other sources of authority.

Aside from education and experience, which are of importance in any type of work, the main thing an inspector should have is "common sense"—an attribute which isn't so common as most homespun philosophers would have us believe.

Besides knowing all that is worth knowing about his particular job, the inspector must come in contact daily with numerous men of varying personalities—who frequently resent having their work criticized. Tact and diplomacy should be exercised; arguments must be avoided.

Types of Inspection

The two general types of inspection are visual and mechanical. A visual inspection is made by simply looking at an object—to determine whether it conforms to the general rules of good workmanship. A mechanical inspection is made with a machine or instruments, designed to tell exactly whether an article meets specific requirements.

In order to make a visual inspection, a man should have a wide knowledge of mechanics. He should know what a scratch can do to a sheet of alclad; he must recognize the appearance of anodized aluminum; he should know all about small parts and their uses; he should be able to recognize a good or bad rivet, or a doubtful specimen of welding, and so forth.

Mechanical inspection necessitates a more specific, or academic knowledge of various types of work—and can therefore be mastered by persons of comparatively little experience. Some of the more common methods of mechanical inspection will be discussed shortly.

The two types of inspection are designed to determine two general causes for rejection:

(1) Whether the finished part deviates from some clearly defined requirements (as set forth in drawings, specifications, etc.).

(2) Whether the finished part deviates from some well-established rule of good workmanship, which may or may not be covered by a drawing or specification.

In government work, almost any violation of good shop practice will be covered by some specification. But even if this is not the case, the government requires that all its work be in accordance with the best commercial practices or standards. Generally speaking, manufacturers are more than willing to abide by this "unwritten law" on any job, because in aircraft work there is no excuse for poor craftsmanship.

General items of inspection which are ordinarily covered by drawings, specifications, etc., are:

(1) Material.
(2) Gage and dimensions.
(3) Heat treatment.
(4) Finish.
(5) Rivets—type, size, etc.
(6) Standard parts and their treatment.
(7) Special parts and their treatment.

Routine deviations from good workmanship are:

(1) Cracks, scratches, or mutilations.
(2) Sharp bends, bad folds, wrinkles, or "oil cans."
(3) Presence of extraneous matter.
(4) Improper tightening and locking of bolts.
(5) Lost motion of moving parts.
(6) Paint on moving parts.
(7) Dirt or oil on parts to be welded, painted, etc.
(8) Lack of insulation between dissimilar metals.
(9) Rinsing and drying of parts after heat treatment.
(10) Extraneous matter on jigs and fixtures.
(11) Improper bend radii.

Since the detailed inspection procedure for each factory and each airplane varies, it is impossible to describe in this book all the inspection methods now being used. However, the more important routines might be listed as follows:

Magnetic inspection—a method of detecting flaws on and below the surface of metals. This process does not apply to nonferrous metals, which cannot be magnetized. Parts to receive this inspection must be thoroughly clean—free of oil, grease, scale, and dirt. However, a thin coat of paint or lacquer will not interfere and should not be removed.

First the part is clamped between two electrical "heads" and sprayed thoroughly with "inspection fluid," a light black petroleum distillate containing "magnaflux paste" or iron oxide. An electrical current—with an intensity of from 500 to 6000 amperes, depending on the size of the part—is then passed through the heads, magnetizing the metal to be examined. This magnetization causes the inspection fluid to adhere and align itself along the lines of any defects that may be present in the metal.

The two types of magnetic (often called "magnaflux") inspection are circular and longitudinal. Circular magnetization causes defects to be revealed in long parts—such as longitudinal cracks, seams, inclusions,—and sometimes radial defects in circular parts. For defects that are essentially circumferential, longitudinal magnetization is preferred. The type of magnetic inspection depends entirely on the way the part is clamped between the electrical heads.

Magnetic inspection is of particular importance on parts that have been welded. Parts that pass the inspection are usually stamped with an *M*.

Rockwell hardness testing—a method of determining the hardness and tensile strengths of metals. This is accomplished on a precision-built Rockwell machine, the purpose of which is to determine the hardness of one material by comparing it with the known hardness of another material. Known hardnesses are based on values stated in "Moh's Scale," numbered from one to ten, as follows:

1. Talc	6. Feldspar
2. Gypsum	7. Quartz
3. Calcite	8. Topaz
4. Fluorite	9. Sapphire (or Corundum) ruby
5. Apatite	10. Diamond

The diamond, being the hardest material known to science, makes the best and most accurate "penetrator" for the Rockwell machine. Its purpose as a penetrator is to determine the hardness of a material by means of a gage which will show how deeply it is able to penetrate the material when a "kilogram load" is applied. A kilogram load is weight or pressure measured in terms of kilograms, each of which is the equivalent of 2.2 pounds.

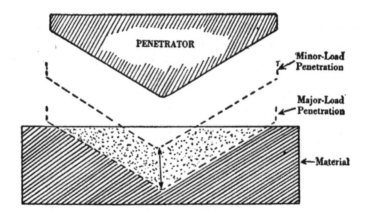

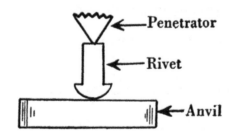

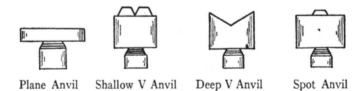

Plane Anvil   Shallow V Anvil   Deep V Anvil   Spot Anvil

Fig. 85. Rockwell Hardness Testing

In using the Rockwell machine, a 10 kilogram (kg.) load is usually applied first; this is called the "minor load." A reading is made to determine the degree of penetration at this point, then a "major load" is applied. The latter may be as little as 60 kg. or as much as 150 kg. A second reading is made to ascertain the major-load penetration, and the load is removed. Hardness is then calculated as the difference between the major and minor loads.

The two most popular penetrators used in the Rockwell machine are called "ball" and "brale." The ball penetrator is of steel, while the brale penetrator is the above-mentioned diamond type.

Making a test on a Rockwell machine requires about five or ten seconds. Readings are expressed with nine different letter prefixes, the letter denoting the type penetrator used and the amount of weight applied as the major load:

LETTER PREFIX	PENETRATOR	LOAD
A	Brale	60 Kg.
B	$\frac{1}{16}''$ Ball	100 Kg.
C	Brale	150 Kg.
D	Brale	100 Kg.
E	$\frac{1}{8}''$ Ball	100 Kg.
F	$\frac{1}{16}''$ Ball	60 Kg.
G	$\frac{1}{16}''$ Ball	150 Kg.
H	$\frac{1}{8}''$ Ball	60 Kg.
K	$\frac{1}{8}''$ Ball	150 Kg.

These readings may be transposed into actual pounds per square inch by referring to a chart, whereon values previously arrived at for rapid interpretation will be found (see the Appendix).

Rockwell hardness testing is of particular value when dealing with metals that have been heat-treated; it is the best method of determining whether a heat treatment has been successful.

Some minimum Rockwell readings are:

Alclad, 17ST F–87
Alclad, 24ST F–90
Al. Alloy, 17ST .... E–90 or B–57

Al. Alloy, 24ST ....F–95 or B–65
Normalized Steel ....C–10 to C–25

Brinell hardness testing—virtually the same as Rockwell hardness testing, the chief difference being the fact that the Brinell machine was developed in Sweden and takes somewhat heavier loads.

A 10-mm. steel ball is used as a penetrator in regular Brinell hardness testing; loads start at 500 kg. and increase by 500 kg. up to

FIG. 86. MACHINE FOR ROCKWELL HARDNESS TESTING
(Courtesy of Wilson Mechanical Instrument Co., Inc.)

3000 kg. The light loads are for soft materials, such as pure aluminum, while heavy loads are for materials such as hard steels.

What is called the "baby Brinell" tester does the same job as a "superficial Rockwell" tester; it is designed especially for light loads (as low as 6.4 kg.), which can be used on thin materials—such as alclad skin.

Stripping test—a method of determining the thickness of protective metallic coatings by finding out how long it takes to dissolve such coatings in acid. For example, a solution containing antimony trioxide is used for stripping cadmium plating; this solution dissolves .0001 inch of the plating for every twenty seconds of time required by the test. Therefore, one hundred seconds would be required to remove the regular .0005 inch cadmium coating.

Naturally, this test can be used only on occasional parts. If its results are not satisfactory, the chemicals used in the plating process must be changed.

Salt-spray test—verifies the corrosion resistance of a metal. In this test, a 20 per cent salt solution is atomized and sprayed on the test material for a period of several hours.

Paint tests—are numerous, some of them rather expensive. However, aircraft inspectors have found that their eyes and thumb nails will tell them about all they need to know in examining any paint job. First, the job should be inspected visually to see whether the coating is smooth and free of blisters or bumps. Then the paint surface should be scratched with the thumb nail in out-of-the-way spots, such as corners, where poor workmanship is most likely to be present. If the scratching makes only a slight impression on the surface, the job is a good one. On the other hand, if the coating peels off, revealing a sticky undersurface, the work must be rejected.

Dimensional inspections—are made with the measuring instruments, templates, etc., previously described. When templates or other patterns are used, this is just a matter of comparison. But, when using measuring instruments, blueprints and specifications must be referred to in order to find out whether the size of the part being inspected is reasonably accurate.

Soap-and-water tests—reveal defects in supposedly watertight hulls, tanks, or other sections. The ordinary water test is made simply by dipping or spraying with water. Soap-and-water tests are used mainly on gas tanks. During this inspection, the tank is filled with compressed air while its exterior surfaces are coated with soap and water; soap bubbles reveal the presence of leaks.

Stress-and-strain tests—made on machines, designed to stretch or compress sections of metal. Stress and strain data, as outlined in Chapter 5, are obtained with scribers and measuring instruments which reveal the elastic limit, yield point, etc.

Anodic test—shows whether a part has been anodized satisfactorily, and is accomplished with dry cell batteries and an ordinary electric doorbell. Positive and negative wires, which are attached to the batteries and bell, are applied to the surface of the anodized part. If the part is properly anodized, it will not conduct the electrical current. Otherwise, the doorbell will ring.

APPENDIX

TABLE 1
WEIGHTS AND SPECIFIC GRAVITIES

Substance	Weight Lb. per Cu. Ft.	Specific Gravity	Substance	Weight Lb. per Cu. Ft.	Specific Gravity
METALS, ALLOYS, ORES			TIMBER, U. S. SEASONED		
Aluminum, cast, hammered	165	2.55-2.75	Moisture Content by Weight:		
Aluminum, bronze	481	7.7	Seasoned timber 15 to 20%		
Brass, cast, rolled	534	8.4-8.7	Green timber up to 50%		
Bronze, 7.9 to 14% Sn	509	7.4-8.9	Ash, white, red	40	0.62-0.65
Copper, cast, rolled	556	8.8-9.0	Cedar, white, red	22	0.32-0.38
Copper ore, pyrites	262	4.1-4.3	Chestnut	41	0.66
Gold, cast, hammered	1205	19.25-19.3	Cypress	30	0.48
Iron, cast, pig	450	7.2	Fir, Douglas spruce	32	0.51
Iron, wrought	485	7.6-7.9	Fir, eastern	25	0.40
Iron, steel	490	7.8-7.9	Elm, white	45	0.72
Iron, spiegel-eisen	468	7.5	Hemlock	29	0.42-0.52
Iron, ferro-silicon	437	6.7-7.3	Hickory	49	0.74-0.84
Iron ore, hematite	325	5.2	Locust	46	0.73
Iron ore, hematite in bank	160-180	------	Maple, hard	43	0.68
Iron ore, hematite loose	130-160	------	Maple, white	33	0.53
Iron ore, limonite	237	3.6-4.0	Oak, chestnut	54	0.86
Iron ore, magnetite	315	4.9-5.2	Oak, live	59	0.95
Iron slag	172	2.5-3.0	Oak, red, black	41	0.65
Lead	710	11.37	Oak, white	46	0.74
Lead ore, galena	465	7.3-7.6	Pine, Oregon	32	0.51
Manganese	475	7.2-8.0	Pine, red	30	0.48
Manganese ore, pyrolusite	259	3.7-4.6	Pine, white	26	0.41
Mercury	849	13.6	Pine, yellow, long-leaf	44	0.70
Nickel	565	8.9-9.2	Pine, yellow, short-leaf	38	0.61
Nickel, monel metal	556	8.8-9.0	Poplar	30	0.48
Platinum, cast, hammered	1330	21.1-21.5	Redwood, California	26	0.42
Silver, cast, hammered	656	10.4-10.6	Spruce, white, black	27	0.40-0.46
Tin, cast, hammered	459	7.2-7.5	Walnut, black	38	0.61
Tin ore, cassiterite	418	6.4-7.0	Walnut, white	26	0.41
Zinc, cast, rolled	440	6.9-7.2			
Zinc ore, blende	253	3.9-4.2			

Courtesy of Bethlehem Steel Co.

TABLE 2
COLORS OF STEEL AT VARIOUS TEMPERATURES

Degrees Centigrade	Degrees Fahrenheit	Colors
400	752	Red, visible in dark
474	885	Red, visible in twilight
525	975	Red, visible in daylight
581	1077	Red, visible in sunlight
700	1292	Dark red
800	1472	Dull Cherry-red
900	1652	Cherry-red
1000	1832	Bright Cherry-red
1100	2012	Orange-red
1200	2192	Orange-yellow
1300	2372	Yellow-white
1400	2552	White welding heat
1500	2732	Brilliant white
1600	2912	Dazzling white (or bluish white)

TABLE 3
CONDITIONS FOR HEAT TREATMENT OF ALUMINUM ALLOYS

Alloy	Solution Heat Treatment				Precipitation Heat Treatment[4]		
	Temperature, Deg. F.	Approximate Time of Heating	Quench[2]	Temper Designation	Temperature, Deg. F.	Time of Aging	Temper Designation
17S	930–950	(1)	Cold water		Room	4 days(3)	17S-T
A17S	930–950	(1)	Cold water		Room	4 days(3)	A17S-T
24S	910–930	(1)	Cold water		Room	4 days(3)	24S-T
53S	960–980	(1)	Cold water	53S-W	315–325 or 345–355	18 hours or 8 hours	53S-T
61S	960–980	(1)	Cold water	61S-W	315–325 or 345–355	18 hours or 8 hours	61S-T

1 In a molten nitrate bath, the time varies from 10 to 60 minutes depending upon the size of the load and the thickness of the material. In an air furnace, proper allowance must be made for a slower rate of bringing the load up to temperature. For heavy material a longer time at temperature may be necessary.

2 It is essential that the quench be made with a minimum time loss in transfer from the furnace.

3 More than 90 per cent of the maximum properties are obtained during the first day of aging.

4 Precipitation heat treatment at elevated temperatures is patented.

Courtesy of Aluminum Co. of America

TABLE 4

AGING DETAILS

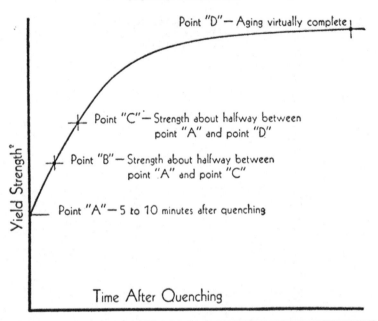

Point "D" — Aging virtually complete

Point "C" — Strength about halfway between point "A" and point "D"

Point "B" — Strength about halfway between point "A" and point "C"

Point "A" — 5 to 10 minutes after quenching

Yield Strength[2]

Time After Quenching

Alloy	Yield Strength,[1] Lb./Sq. In. at Point "A"	Temperature of Metal				
		70°F.			32°F. ([3])	
		Time to Reach Point			Time to Reach Point	
		B	C	D	B	C
17S([4])	18,000	2 hr.	4 hr.	4 days	3½ days	......
A17S	9,500	1½ hr.	6 hr.	4 days	....	......
24S([4])	22,000	1 hr.	2 hr.	1 day	1 day	4 days
61S	9,000	2½ hr.	12 hr.	1 month	....	......

[1] Typical values.
[2] Ultimate tensile strength increases at approximately the same rate.
[3] When material is returned to room temperature, aging proceeds at normal rate.
[4] Alloys 17S and 24S show no increase in strength in 7 days at a temperature of 0°F.

Courtesy of Aluminum Co. of America

TABLE 5

COMMERCIAL ALUMINUM ALLOYS

Type*	Alcoa Alloy	COMPOSITION (per cent)				
		Cu	Fe or Mn	Si	Mg	Other
		Non-Heat-Treated Casting Alloys				
I	173	7.0	......	...	...	2.0 Sn
	C113	7.5	1.2 Fe	4.0	...	2.0 Zn
	645	2.5	1.5 Fe	...	...	11.0 Zn
	B113	7.5	1.2 Fe	1.5	...	......
II	112	7.5	1.2 Fe	...	...	2.0 Zn
	216	....	......	...	6.0	......
	A214	....	......	...	3.8	2.0 Zn
	109	12.0	......	...	...	......
	12	8.0	......	...	...	......
	214	....	......	...	3.8	......
	212	8.0	1.0 Fe	1.2	...	....
	B214	....	......	1.8	3.8	....
III	172	7.8	......	2.5	...	......
	A108	4.5	......	5.5	...	......
	108	4.0	......	3.0	...	....
	356	....	......	7.0	0.3	......
	43	....	......	5.0	...	......
		Heat-Treated Casting Alloys (a)				
I	220(b)	....	......	...	10.0	......
	122	10.0	1.2 Fe	...	0.2	......
II	D195	5.5	......	0.7	...	......
	142	4.0	......	...	1.5	2.0 Ni
	195	4.0	......	...	...	......
	B195	4.5	......	3.0	...	......
III	355	1.3	......	5.0	0.5	......
	A355	1.4	0.8 Mn	5.0	0.5	0.8 Ni
	356	...	......	7.0	0.3	......
(c)	A132	0.8	0.8 Fe	12.0	1.0	2.5 Ni
		Heat-Treated Wrought Alloys (a)				
I	11S	5.5	......	...	...	0.5 Pb+0.5 Bi
II	61S	0.25	......	0.6	1.0	0.25 Cr
	53S	...	......	0.7	1.3	0.25 Cr
	A51S	..	......	1.0	0.6	0.25 Cr
	17S	4.0	0.5 Mn	...	0.5	......
III	25S	4.5	0.8 Mn	0.8	...	......
	70S	1.0	0.7 Mn	...	0.4	10.0 Zn
	18S	4.0	......	...	0.5	2.0 Ni
	14S	4.4	0.8 Mn	0.8	0.4	......
	24S	4.4	0.5 Mn	...	1.5	......
(c)	32S	0.8	......	12.0	1.0	0.8 Ni
		Non-Heat-Treated Wrought Alloys				
II	56S	..	0.1 Mn	...	5.2	0.1 Cr
III	4S	...	1.2 Mn	...	1.0	......
	52S	...	......	...	2.5	0.25 Cr
	3S	...	1.2 Mn	...	...	......

* Indicates relative machinability. Type I alloys have best machining characteristics.
(a) Heat treated as usually sold, namely a solution treatment followed by aging at room or elevated temperature.
(b) Alloy 220 is not aged.
(c) Alloy cuts freely, but wear on tools may be excessive unless they are tipped with cemented carbide.

Courtesy of Aluminum Co. of America

TABLE 6—HEAT-TREATMENT PROCEDURE FOR STRUCTURAL STEELS

Steel No.	Normalizing Air Cool (deg. F.)	Annealing (deg. F.)	Hardening (deg. F.)	Quenching Medium 65 deg. F.	Tempering (Drawing) Temperatures for Tensile Strength				
					100,000 (deg. F.)	125,000 (deg. F.)	150,000 (deg. F.)	180,000 (deg. F.)	200,000 (deg. F.)
1020	1650-1750	1600-1700	1575-1675	Water					
X1020	1650-1750	1600-1700	1575-1675	Water	a				
1025	1600-1700	1575-1650	1575-1675	Water	875				
1035	1575-1650	1575-1625	1525-1600	Water	1150				
1045	1550-1600	1550-1600	1475-1550	Oil or Water					
1095	1475-1550	1450-1500	1425-1500	Oil	b 1100		1100	850	750
2330	1475-1525	1425-1475	1450-1500	Oil or Water		950	800		
3135	1600-1650	1500-1550	1475-1525	Oil	1250	1050	900	750	650
3140	1600-1650	1500-1550	1475-1525	Oil	1325	1075	925	775	700
X4130	1600-1700	1525-1575	1575-1625	Oil e	d	1050	900	700	575
4140	1600-1650	1525-1575	1525-1575	Oil	1350	1100	1025	825	675
4150	1550-1600	1475-1525	1500-1550	Oil		1275	1175	1050	950
X4340	1550-1625	1325-1575	1475-1550	Oil		1200	1050	950	850
4640	1675-1700	1525-1575	1500-1550	Oil		1200	1050	750	625
6135	1600-1700	1550-1600	1575-1625	Oil	1300	1075	950	800	750
6150	1600-1650	1525-1575	1550-1625	Oil	d e	1200	1000	900	800
6195	1600-1650	1525-1575	1500-1550	Oil	f				
30905	....	g h	i	Oil					
51210	1525-1575	1525-1575	1775-1825 j	Oil	1200	1100	k	750	
51335	....	1525-1575	1775-1850	Oil					1070
52100	1625-1700	1400-1450	1525-1550	Oil	f				
Corrosion Resisting (16-2) l	....	....	....	....	m				
Silicon Chromium (for springs)	....	....	1700-1725	Oil					

Notes for Table

a Draw at 1150° F. for tensile strength of 70,000 lb. per sq. in.
b For spring temper draw at 800 to 900° F. Rockwell Hardness C-40-45.
c Bars or forgings may be quenched in water from 1550-1600° F.
d Air-cooling from the normalizing temperature will produce a tensile strength of approximately 90,000 lb. per sq. in.
e For spring temper draw at 850 to 950° F. Rockwell Hardness C-40-45.
f Draw at 350 to 450° F. to remove quenching strains. Rockwell Hardness C-60-65.
g Anneal at 1600 to 1700° F. to remove residual stresses of welding or cold work. Apply only to steel containing titanium or columbium.
h Hardened by cold work only.
i Anneal at 1900 to 2100° F. to produce maximum softness and corrosion resistance. Cool in air or quench in water.
j Lower side of range for sheet 0.06 inch and under. Middle of range for sheet and wire 0.125 inch. Upper side of range for forgings.
k Not recommended for intermediate tensile strengths because of low impact.
l As desired, subject to government approval. Request for approval shall be accompanied by report of tests, conducted in the presence of inspector, showing results in conformance with requirements of Specification AN-QQ-S-770. (Refer to section G, Heat Treatment of Steel.)
m Draw at approximately 800° F. and cool in air for Rockwell Hardness of C-50.

Appendix

TABLE

STRENGTH AND SPECIFICATION

Alloy and Temper Alcoa	Type	U.T.S. Lbs./Sq. In.	Yield Strength Lbs./Sq. In.
Aluminum-2S-½H	Sheet	16,000	
Aluminum-2S-½H	Rod	17,000	14,000
Aluminum-2S-½H	Tubing	16,000	
Alum. Alloy-14ST	Forging	65,000	50,000
Alum. Alloy-17ST	Tubing	55,000	40,000
Alum. Alloy-17ST	Forging	55,000	30,000
Alum. Alloy-24SO	Sheet	35,000	
Alum. Alloy-24SO	Extrusuion	35,000	
Alum. Alloy-24SO	Rod	35,000	
Alum. Alloy-24ST	Sheet	62,000	40,000
Alum. Alloy-24ST	Extrusion	57,000	42,000
Alum. Alloy-24ST	Bar and Rod	62,000	40,000
Alclad-24SO	Sheet	30,000	
Alclad-24ST	Sheet	56,000	37,000
Alclad-24SRT	Sheet	58,000	46,000
Alum. Alloy-52SO	Sheet	31,000	
Alum. Alloy-52SO	Tubing	29,000	
Alum. Alloy-53ST	Extrusion	32,000	25,000
Alum. Alloy-53ST	Rod	32,000	25,000
Alum. Alloy-53SW	Extrusion	28,000	14,000
Alum. Alloy-#356T4	Sand Casting	26,000	16,000
Alum. Alloy-#195T4	Sand Casting	29, 00	16,000
Alum. Alloy-#220T4	Sand Casting	42,000	25,000
Alum. Alloy-#356T4	Permanent Mold Casting	28,000	18,000
Alum. Alloy-#13	Die Casting	33,000	18,000

Appendix 163

7

NUMBERS FOR ALUMINUM ALLOYS

Army Spec.	Navy Spec.	Federal Spec.	Army-Navy Spec.	S.A.E. Number
57-151-1-½H	47A2-Cond. ½H	QQ-A-561(½H)		25
Federal	46A3-Cond. F	QQ-A-411(F)		25
Federal	44T19-Cond. ½H	WW-T-783(½H)		25
Federal	46A7-GR. 5	QQ-A-367(GR. 5)		26
Federal	44T21-Cond. T	WW-T-786(T)		26
Federal	46A7-GR. 1	QQ-A-367(GR. 1)		26
Federal	46A10-Cond. A	QQ-A-355(A)		24
Federal	46A9-Cond. A	QQ-A-354(A)		24
Federal	46A9-Cond. A	QQ-A-354(A)		24
Federal	47A10-Cond. T	QQ-A-355(T)		24
Federal	46A9-Cond. T	QQ-A-354(T)		24
Federal	46A9-Cond. T	QQ-A-354(T)		24
11067-I	47A8-Cond. A			
11067-II	47A8-Cond. T			
	47A8-Cond. RT			
Federal	47A11-Cond. A	QQ-A-318(A)		201
57-187-3	44T32-Cond. A			201
Federal	46A10-Cond. T	QQ-A-331(T)		
Federal	46A10-Cond. T	QQ-A-331(T)		
Federal	46A10-Cond. W	QQ-A-331(W)		
Federal	46A1-Class 3	QQ-A-601(Cl. 3)	AN-QQ-A-394	323
Federal	46A1-Class 4	QQ-A-601(Cl. 4)	AN-QQ-A-390	38
11309	M-186			324
	46A15-Class 8	QQ-A-596	AN-QQ-A-376	322
57-93-1(Gr. 2)	46A14-Class 1	QQ-A-591		305

TABLE

STRENGTH AND SPECIFICA

Alloy	Type	Min. T.S. Lbs./Sq. In.	Yield Str. Lbs./Sq. In.
Chrome-Moly.	Sheet	90,000	70,000
" "	Bar	125,000	100,000
" "	Bar	125,000	100,000
" "	Rod	125,000	100,000
" "	Tubing	95,000	75,000
" "	Casting	100,000	70,000
" "	Forging	125,000	100,000
" "	Forging	125,000	100,000
" "	Forging		
Corr. and Heat Resist	Sheet	80,000	35,000
Corr. Resist	Sheet	80,000	30,000
" "	Sheet	125,000	75,000
" "	Sheet	150,000	110,000
" "	Bar	*	
" "	Bar	**	
" "	Bar		
" "	Rod	*	
" "	Rod	**	
" "	Tubing	80,000	35,000
" "	Tubing	125,000	75,000
" "	Tubing	80,000	30,000
" "	Casting	70,000	40% of U.T.S.
" "	Casting	70,000	40% of U.T.S.
" "	Forging	"Bar" **	
" "	Forging	175,000 Max.	
Utiloy XX #2 (Corr. Resist)	Casting	89,000	64,000

* U.T.S. decreases inversely with thickness of bar. Up to ½ inch thick, U.T.S. inches thick.

** U.T.S. decreases inversely with thickness of bar. Up to 1-½ inches thick, U.T.S. thick.

TION NUMBERS FOR STEEL

Army Spec.	Navy Spec.	Federal Spec.	Army-Navy Spec.	S.A.E. Number
57-136-8	47S14		AN-QQ-S-684	X-4130
57-107-19	46S23-Gr. A		AN-QQ-S-684	X-4130
10083	46S23-Gr. B			4140
57-107-19	46S23-Gr. A		AN-QQ-S-684	X-4130
57-180-2(A)	44T18-Cond. A			X-4130
57-64-1		QQ-S-681		
	46S23-Gr. A			X-4130
	46S23-Gr. B			4140
57-105				
(W.D. 4135)				4135
56-136-9, Gr. ISS	47S19-Gr. ISS			30905
11068(An.)	47S21(Ann.)			30915
11068(¼H)	47S21(¼H)			30915
11068(½H)	47S21(½H)			30915
10079-	46S18-Type C			
Cond. 1H	Gr. 1			30905
10079-	46S18-Type E			
Cond. 1A	Gr. 7			
	M-286-Cond. A			
11079-	46S18-Type C			
Cond. 1H	Gr. 1			30905
11079-	46S18-Type E			
Cond. 1A	Gr. 7			
	WAS 44T27-		AN-WW-T-855	
	Temp. A		Gr. A	30905
	WAS 44T27-		AN-WW-T-855	
	Temp. ¼H		Gr. B	
	WAS 44T25-		AN-WW-T-858	
	Gr. 1SC			
	46S27-Gr. 1			
	46S27-Gr. 7			
11079	46S18-Gr. 7E			
	M-286-Cond. A			
Comm.	Comm.	Comm.	Comm.	

125,000 Lbs./Sq. In., decreasing to U.T.S. = 105,000 Lbs./Sq. In. for bar 1-¼

100,000 Lbs./Sq. In., decreasing to U.T.S. 95,000 Lbs./Sq. In. for bar 3 inches

TABLE 9

STANDARD COLOR CHART FOR RAW MATERIALS

Commercial Spec.	Material	Color	Form	Army Spec.	Navy Spec.
SAE 1020	Commercial Steel	Red	Bar	57–107–9B	46–S–22
SAE 1095	Steel	White	Bar	57–136–2	
SAE 1095	Spring Steel Temp.	Blue & Brown	Sheet	57–136–6	47–S–15
SAE 2320	Spring Steel Ann.	Blue & Orange	Sheet	57–107–12	
SAE 2330	Steel	Blue & Alum.	Bar	57–107–17b	
SAE 3120	Nickel Steel	Yellow	Bar	57–107–26	46–S–21b
SAE 3230	Chrome-Nickel Steel	Yellow & White	Bar		
SAE 3240	Steel	Blue & White	Bar	57–107–4	
SAE 3250	Chrome-Nickel Steel	Blue & White	Bar	57–107–6	
	Steel	Brown & Green	Tube		
M286	Income Metal Comm.	Yellow & Red	Bar		M286
Gr. 1 Spec.	Stainless Steel Comm.	Red, White & Green	Bar		
	Quenched St. St. 85000# 115,000/D"			Gr. 1 (Spec.)	
Gr. 1 ty C.	Stainless Steel	Red, White & Blue	Bar		46–S–18C
		Red & White	Sheet		47–S–19b
			Bar		46–S–18C
			Tube		44–T–25a
Gr. 7 ty E.	Stainless Steel	Green & White	Sheet		47–S–21
			Bar	11068–A	46–S–18C
SAE 4130	Chrome-Moly. Steel	Blue	Tube	57–180–3b	44–T–27A int.
			Bar	57–107–19b	46–S–23E Gr. A
			Tube	57–182–2c	44–T–18C
			Sheet	57–136–8c	47–S–14B
SAE 4140	Chrome-Moly. 35 to 40 Car.	Blue & Red	Bar	10083	46–S–23E Gr. B

TABLE 9—Continued

STANDARD COLOR CHART FOR RAW MATERIALS

Commercial Spec.	Material	Color	Form	Army Spec.	Navy Spec.
2S— H	Stainless Steel Ann.	Red & Purple			M253A H. T.
	Allegheny Steel Reg.	Brown & White			46–A–3C
	Allegheny Steel Ann.	Brown & Red			44–T–19a
	Monel Metal	Black & Brown			47–A–20
	Aluminum	White & Black	Bar	QQA411	46–A–9B Cond. T
			Tube		47–A–10 int. cond. T
			Sheet		44–T–28A Cond. T
24ST	Alum. Alloy Temp.	Orange	Bar & Ex.	57–152–6 ty 2	46–A–9B Cond. A
			Sheet		47–A–10 Cond. A
24SO	Alum. Alloy Ann.	Orange & Red	Tube	57–152–6 ty 1	44–T–28 Cond. A
			Bar		M277B
			Sheet		46–A–10A Cond. T
14ST	Alum. Alloy Forging	Yellow & Black	Tube		47–A–9
53ST	Alum. Alloy	Yellow & Brown	Bar		44–T–24
4 SO	Alum. Manganese	White & Fawn	Bar & Ex.		
			Sheet		
			Tube		
17ST	Alum. Alloy Temp.	Fawn	Sheet		47–A–3b Cond. T
			Bar		46–A–4c Cond. T
			Tube		44–T–21b Cond. T
17S	Rivet Wire	No Color			4345C Gr. C
A17S	Rivet Wire	Red			4345C
17SO	Alum. Alloy Ann.	Fawn & Red	Sheet		47–A–3b Cond. A

167

TABLE 9—*Continued*

STANDARD COLOR CHART FOR RAW MATERIALS

Commercial Spec.	Material	Color	Form	Army Spec.	Navy Spec.
			Bar		46–A–4c Cond. A
			Tube		44–T–21b Cond. A
XA52SO	Alum. Alloy	Green & Fawn	Sheet	11072–A	47–A–11 Cond. A
			Tube	11073	44–T–32B Cond. A
3 S	Alum. Manganese	Black & Green	Sheet		44–T–20a
17ST Alc.	Alclad Sheet	Black & Fawn	Sheet		47–A–6A Cond. T
17SO Alc.	Alclad Sheet	Black, Fawn & Red	Sheet	11067–11	47–A–6a Cond. A
24ST Alc.	Alclad Sheet	Black & Orange			47–A–8 int. Cond. A
	Everdur	Black & Alum.			Commercial
AM4–4	Magnesium Alloy				
	Dow Metal	Black & Blue			
	Ext. Aluminum Bars	Green		QQ–B–66	46–B–17a
	Tobin Bronze	Black			
	Mang. Bronze	Green & Red	Bar	QQ–B–721	46–B–15c
			Cast.	QQ–B–726	
	Phosp. Bronze	Green & Alum.	Bar	QQ–B–746	46–B–14e
			Sheet		46–B–14e
			Cast.		46–B–5g Gr. 11
	Silic. Bronze	Green & Orange	Bar	QQ–B–6–11	47–B–2f
	Comm. Brass	No Color	Sheet		47–B–2f
			Tube		47–B–2f
	Naval Brass	Yellow & Green	Bar	57–162	46–B–6i
	#20 Lumen Alloy	No Color	Bar		
24SRT	Sheet	Orange & White	Sheet	11067–111	47–A–8

TABLE 10

STANDARD SIZES OF RIVETS WITH CHAMFERED SHANK

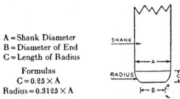

A = Shank Diameter
B = Diameter of End
C = Length of Radius

Formulas
C = 0.25 × A
Radius = 0.3125 × A

Diameter of Rivet, Inches	B, Inches	Diameter of Rivet, Inches	B, Inches
1/16	0.047	5/32	0.118
3/32	0.071	3/16	0.137
1/8	0.092	1/4	0.185

Length, Inches	1/16 A	1/16 B	3/32 A	3/32 B	1/8 A	1/8 B	5/32 A	5/32 B	3/16 A	3/16 B	1/4 A	1/4 B
1/16	X	X										
1/8	X	X	X	X	X	X						
3/16	X	X	X	X	X	X						
1/4	X	X	X	X	X	X	X	X	X	X	X	X
5/16	X	X	X	X	X	X	X	X	X	X	X	X
3/8	X	X	X	X	X	X	X	X	X	X	X	X
7/16	X		X	X	X	X	X	X	X	X	X	X
1/2	X		X	X	X	X	X	X	X	X	X	X
9/16			X	X	X	X	X	X	X	X	X	X
5/8			X		X	X	X	X	X	X	X	X
11/16			X		X	X	X	X	X	X	X	X
3/4			X		X	X	X	X	X	X	X	X
13/16					X		X	X	X	X	X	X
7/8					X		X	X	X	X	X	X
15/16					X		X		X	X	X	X
1					X		X		X	X	X	X
1 1/8							X		X		X	X
1 1/4							X				X	X
1 3/8									X		X	X
1 1/2									X		X	X
1 5/8											X	
1 3/4											X	
1 7/8											X	
2											X	

Diameter (Inches) and Head Type

*{A covers standard round, button, brazier or mushroom heads.
{B covers standard flat, flat countersunk or oval countersunk heads.

Courtesy of Aluminum Co. of America

Appendix

TABLE 11

CENTIGRADE AND FAHRENHEIT TEMPERATURE EQUIVALENTS

Cent.	Fahr.	Cent.	Fahr.	Cent.	Fahr.	Cent.	Fahr.
0	32.0	26	78.8	52	125.6	78	172.4
1	33.8	27	80.6	53	127.4	79	174.2
2	35.6	28	82.4	54	129.2	80	176.0
3	37.4	29	84.2	55	131.0	81	177.8
4	39.2	30	86.0	56	132.8	82	179.6
5	41.0	31	87.8	57	134.6	83	181.4
6	42.8	32	89.6	58	136.4	84	183.2
7	44.6	33	91.4	59	138.2	85	185.0
8	46.4	34	93.2	60	140.0	86	186.8
9	48.2	35	95.0	61	141.8	87	188.6
10	50.0	36	96.8	62	143.6	88	190.4
11	51.8	37	98.6	63	145.4	89	192.2
12	53.6	38	100.4	64	147.2	90	194.0
13	55.4	39	102.2	65	149.0	91	195.8
14	57.2	40	104.0	66	150.8	92	197.6
15	59.0	41	105.8	67	152.6	93	199.4
16	60.8	42	107.6	68	154.4	94	201.2
17	62.6	43	109.4	69	156.2	95	203.0
18	64.4	44	111.2	70	158.0	96	204.8
19	66.2	45	113.0	71	159.8	97	206.6
20	68.0	46	114.8	72	161.6	98	208.4
21	69.8	47	116.6	73	163.4	99	210.2
22	71.6	48	118.4	74	165.2	100	212.0
23	73.4	49	120.2	75	167.0		
24	75.2	50	122.0	76	168.8		
25	77.0	51	123.8	77	170.6		

To convert Fahrenheit to Centigrade, subtract 32, multiply by 5 and divide by 9.

To convert Centigrade to Fahrenheit, multiply by 9, divide by 5 and add 32.

TABLE 12

BEND RADII INFORMATION

24SO and 24SO ALCLAD		24ST and 24ST ALCLAD	
THICKNESS	INSIDE RAD. : 1/64	THICKNESS	INSIDE RAD. : 1/64
.016 to .025 incl.	1/32	.016 to .040 incl.	1/16
.030 to .040 incl.	1/16	.045 to .080 incl.	1/8
.045 to .080 incl.	3/32	.091	3/16
.091	1/8	.128 to 5/32 incl.	7/16
.128 to 5/32 incl.	5/16	3/16 and 1/4 use 24SO for forming	
3/16	7/16		

24ST material to be used always when the bend is straight, except as noted *

 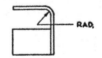

24SO material to be used ONLY when there is reverse bending or severe forming.

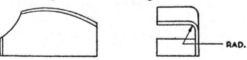

NOTE: Use 24SO when sections are to be formed on the draw bench, or if a small radius is required for straight bends.

TABLE 13—JOGGLE CHART FOR EXTRUDED SECTIONS

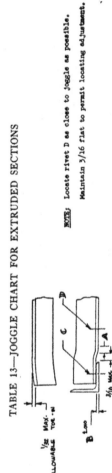

1/32 Max. Allowable Tol.

3/16 Max.

NOTE: Locate rivet D as close to joggle as possible.

Maintain 3/16 flat to permit locating adjustment.

	EXTRUDED SECTION	DIMENSIONS			LENGTH OF JOGGLE "A" WHEN "B" =					
					1/32	1/16	3/32	1/8	3/16	1/4
⌐ (L)	78P	1/2	x 1/2	x 3/32	5/16	3/8	7/16	1/2	11/16	3/4
	K-6240	9/16	x 9/16	x .040	5/16	3/8	7/16	1/2	11/16	3/4
	K-13624	5/8	x 5/8	x 1/16	3/8	7/16	1/2	5/8	3/4	13/16
	K-5401	3/4	x 3/4	x 1/16	3/8	7/16	1/2	5/8	13/16	15/16
	K-78C	3/4	x 3/4	x 3/32	3/8	7/16	1/2	11/16	13/16	7/8
	K-78J	1	x 1	x 1/16	3/8	7/16	1/2	11/16	13/16	7/8
	K-78P	1	x 1	x 3/32	3/8	7/16	1/2	11/16	13/16	7/8
	K-77B	1 1/4	x 1/4	x 1/8	7/16	1/2	5/8	3/4	7/8	15/16
	K-78Y	1 1/4	x 1/4	x 3/32	7/16	1/2	5/8	3/4	7/8	15/16
	K-77F	1 1/2	x 1/2	x 1/8	7/16	1/2	5/8	3/4	7/8	15/16
	K-11657	1 1/2	x 1/2	x 5/32	7/16	1/2	5/8	3/4	7/8	15/16
	K-78L	1 5/16	x 3/4	x 5/32	7/16	1/2	5/8	3/4	7/8	15/16
⌐_ (L)	766	7/8	x 7/8	x 1/16	5/16	3/8	7/16	9/16	11/16	3/4
	K-1559	7/8	x 7/8	x .060	5/16	3/8	7/16	9/16	11/16	3/4
	K-1515	1	x 9/16	x .090	5/16	3/8	7/16	9/16	11/16	3/4
	K-1298	1 1/2	x 5/8	x 1/16	5/8	3/8	7/16	9/16	11/16	3/4
	K-5009	7/8	x 11/16	x 3/4	3/8	7/16	1/2	5/8	5/8	13/16
	K-778	1 5/16	x 3/4	x 5/32	3/8	7/16	1/2	5/8	5/8	13/16
⌐⌐ (Z)	K-9048	7/8	x 5/8	x .045	3/8	7/16	1/2	5/8	11/16	3/4
	K-775	7/8	x 9/16	x .060	3/8	7/16	1/2	5/8	11/16	3/4
	K-9047	1 1/2	x 1/2	x .090	7/16	1/2	5/8	3/4	13/16	7/8
	K-11824	1 1/2	x 13/16	x 1/16	7/16	1/2	5/8	3/4	7/8	15/16
	K-8669	7/8	x 13/16	x .075	3/8	7/16	1/2	5/8	5/8	3/4
	K-14040	7/8	x 5/8	x .045	7/16	3/8	1/2	1/2	11/16	7/8
	K-11886	5/8	x 1/2	x .035	7/16	1/2	5/8	3/4	13/16	7/8
	K-13686	1 1/8	x 11/16	x .090	7/16	1/2	5/8	3/4	13/16	7/8
	K-11270	1 1/8	x 13/16	x .060	7/16	1/2	5/8	3/4	13/16	15/16
	K-5010	1 1/4	x 9/16	x .075	7/16	1/2	5/8	3/4	7/8	15/16
	K-11871	1 1/4	x 7/8	x .070	7/16	1/2	5/8	3/4	7/8	15/16
	K-1060	1 1/4	x 3/4	x 5/32	7/16	1/2	5/8	3/4	7/8	15/16

172

TABLE 14

ABBREVIATIONS USED ON AIRCRAFT BLUEPRINTS

Accessory	ACCES.		Chief Engineer	CH. ENG.
Actual	ACT.		Circumference	CIR.
Adjust	ADJ.		Cold Rolled Steel	CRST.
After	AFT.		Commercial	COML.
Aileron	AIL.		Compartment	COMPT.
Air Corps (Army)	A.C.		Condition	COND.
Alclad	ALC., AL.		Conduit	CONDT.
Aluminum	ALUM.		Corporation	CORP.
Alum. alloy	AL. alloy		Control	CONT.
Aluminum Company of			Continued	CONTD.
America	ALCOA.		Corrigated	CORR.
Aluminum bronze	AL. BR.		Counterbore	CBORE.
Aluminum casting	AL. C.		Countersink	CSK.
And	&		Counterdrill	CDRILL.
Anodize	ANOD.		Change Order	C.O.
Ammunition	AMM.		Chord Line	C.L.
Approximately	APPROX.		Center Section	C.S.
Army and Navy	AN		Counter Press	C' PRESS
Army-Navy accepted	ASA		Decimal	DEC.
Assembly	ASSEM.		Desired	DES.
Attached	ATT.		Developed Length	D.L.
Auxiliary	AUXIL.		Developed Width	D.W.
Baggage	BAG.		Diagonal	DIAG.
Base Line	BL.		Diameter	DIA. D.
Bend Allowance	B.A.		Dimension	DIM.
Bend Down	B.D.		Distance	DIST.
Bend Line	B.L.		Down	DN.
Bend Up	B.U.		Draftsman	DFTSMN.
Bill of Material	B/M		Drafting	DFTG.
Birmingham Wire Gage	B.W.G.		Drafting Room Manual	D.R.M.
Between	BETWN.		Drawing	DWG.
Blueprint	PRINT		Drill Rod	D.R.
Bracket	BPKT.		Each	EA.
Brazier	BRAZ.		Elevator	ELEV.
Brown-Sharpe	B. & S.		Empennage	EMP.
Bulkhead	BLKD.		Engine	ENG.
Buttock Line	B.L.		Equipment	EQUIP.
Cancelled	CAN.		Equivalent	EQUIV.
Cast Iron	C.I.		Example	I.E.
Casting	CSTG.		Experimental	X.
Center	CTR.		Extension	EXTEN.
Center to Center	C.C.		Extra	EXT.
Center to Gravity	C/G		Extrusion	EXTR.
Change	CHNG.		Fairing	FAIR.
Center Line	CL.		Federal	FED.
Charge	CHG.		Feet	FT.
Check	CHK.		Figure	FIG.

TABLE 14—*Continued*

ABBREVIATIONS USED ON AIRCRAFT BLUEPRINTS

Fillet	FIL.	Music Wire	M.W.
Fillister Head	FIL. HD.	Nacelle	NAC.
Finish	FIN.	Naval Aircraft Factory	N.A.F.
Fitting	FIT.	Number	No. #
Flat Head	F.H.	Number Required	NO. REQ.
Flexible	FLEX.	Object	OBJ.
Flotation	FLOT.	Obsolete	OBS.
Forward	FORWD.	Ounce	OZ.
Front	FR.	Open	OP.
Front Spar	F.S.	Order	ORD.
Fuselage	FUS.	Outboard	OUTBD.
Gauge	GA.	Outside Diameter	O.D.
General	GENL.	Overall	O.V.
Generator	GEN.	Oxygen	OXY.
Head	HD.	Opposite Hand	Op. H.
Heat treated	H.T.	On Center	O.C.
Hexagon	HEX.	Outer Panel	O.P.
Horizontal	HOR.	Piece	PC.
High speed Steel	HST.	Pitch Diameter	P.D.
Hydraulic	HYD.	Port	PORT
Inboard	INBD.	Plate	PL.
Inch	IN.	Position	POS.
Inside Diameter	I.D.	Pound	Lb.
Inspector	INSP.	Preliminary	PRELIM.
Inspector of Naval		Production	PROD.
Aircraft	I.N.A.	Production Engineer	PROD. ENG.
Installation	INSTAL.	Propeller	PROP.
Invisible	INV.	Question	QUEST.
Landing Gear	LDG. GR.	Radius	
Leading Edge	L.E.	Reference	REF.
Left	L.	Reinforcement	REINF.
Left Hand	L.H.	Release	REL.
Letter	LET.	Required	REQ.
Longeron	LONG.	Requirements	REQMTS.
Lubrication	LUB.	Right	R.
Machine	MACH.	Right Hand	R.H.
Maintenance	MAIN.	Round	RD.
Manufacture	MFG.	Round Head	RD. HD.
Material	MATL.	Rubber	RUBB.
Maximum	MAX.	Section	SECTN.
Medium	MED.	Sheet	SH.
Micrometer	MIC.	Special	SPCL.
Minimum	MIN.	Specification	SPEC.
Miscellaneous	MISC.	Square Stabilizer	SQ. STAB.
Mold Line	M.L.	Society of Automotive	
Mount	MT.	Engineers	S.A.E.
Mounting	MTG.	Standard	STAN.

TABLE 14—*Continued*

ABBREVIATIONS USED ON AIRCRAFT BLUEPRINTS

Starboard	STBD.	System	SYST.
Station	STA.	Temperature	TEMP.
Steel	STL.	Tensile Strength	TEN. STR.
Sheet Steel	SH. ST.	Thick	THK.
Stiffner	STIF.	Thread	THD.
Stock Length	S.L.	Trailing Edge	T.E.
Stock Width	S.W.	True Length	T.L.
Structure	STRUC.	United States Standard	U.S.S.
Support	SUP.	Vertical	VERT.
Switch	SW.	Waterline	W.L.
Symmetrical	SYM.	Experimental Weight	X.WT.

Engineering Group Names

Aero-Dynamics	AD.	Tail Group	T.G.
Armament	ARM.	Fuselage	FUS.
Center Section	C.S.	Landing Gear	L.G.
Controls	CONT.	Plumbing	PLUMG.
Electrical	ELECT.	Power Plant	P.P.
Empennage	EMP.	Wing	WING

TABLE 15

AIRCRAFT FINISH CODE

A.B.C. .... Aluminum Bitumastic Compound

A.B.P. .... Aluminum Bitumastic Paint

A.D. .... Aluminum Dope

A.E. .... Aluminum Enamel

A.F. .... Aluminum Foil

A.K.V. .... Aluminum Bakelite Varnish

A.L. .... Aluminum Lacquer

A.M.S. .... Aluminum Metal Spray

A.P. .... Aluminum Prime (Red Oxide)

A.P.P. .... Aluminum Acid Proof Paint

B. .... Bake

B.A.V. .... Black Asphalt Varnish (Acid Proof)

B.C. .... Bitumastic Compound

B.E. .... Blue Enamel

B.K.E. .... Black Enamel

B.K.L. .... Black Lacquer

B.L. .... Blue Lacquer

TABLE 15—*Continued*

AIRCRAFT FINISH CODE

B.O. .... Boiled Linseed Oil
C. .... Cadmium Plate
C.E.L. .... Cellulose Tape
D. .... Dope
D.B.L. .... Dull Black Lacquer
D.P.P. .... Dope Proof Paint
E. .... Enamel
F.G.B. .... Flat Bronze Green
G.B.E. .... Gloss Black Enamel
G.B.L. .... Gloss Black Lacquer
H.R.O. .... Hot Raw Oil
H.T. .... Heat Treatment
I.B.E. .... Insignia Blue
I.R. .... Insignia Red
I.W. .... Insignia White
K. .... Bakelite
L. .... Lacquer
M.G. .... Marine Glue
N.G.E. .... Navy Gray Enamel
N.G.L. .... Navy Gray Lacquer
N.W.S. .... Non-Water-Tight
P. .... Prime (Red Oxide)
R.P. .... Rust Preventive
S.B. .... Sand Blast
T.P. .... Tinted Primer
V. .... Varnish
W.L.T. .... White Lead Tallow
W.S. .... Water Tight
Y. .... Yellow
Y.D. .... Yellow Dope
Y.E. .... Yellow Enamel
Y.L. .... Yellow Lacquer
Z. .... Anodic Treatment

TABLE 16
DIFFERENT STANDARDS FOR WIRE GAGES IN USE IN THE UNITED STATES

Dimensions of Sizes in Decimal Parts of an Inch

Number of Wire Gage	American or Brown & Sharpe	Birmingham or Stubs' Iron Wire	Washburn & Moen, Worcester, Mass.	W. & M. Steel Music Wire	American S. & W. Co.'s Music Wire Gage	Imperial Wire Gage	Stubs' Steel Wire	U. S. Standard Gage for Sheet and Plate Iron and Steel	Number of Wire Gage
00000000	....	....	....	.0083	....	....	....	....	00000000
0000000	....	....	....	.0087	....	....	....	....	0000000
000000	....	....	....	.0095	.004	.464	....	.46875	000000
00000	....	....	....	.010	.005	.432	....	.4375	00000
0000	.460	.454	.3938	.011	.006	.400	....	.40625	0000
000	.40964	.425	.3625	.012	.007	.372	....	.375	000
00	.3648	.380	.3310	.0133	.008	.348	....	.34375	00
0	.32486	.340	.3065	.0144	.009	.324	....	.3125	0
1	.2893	.300	.2830	.0156	.010	.300	.227	.28125	1
2	.25763	.284	.2625	.0166	.011	.276	.219	.265625	2
3	.22942	.259	.2437	.0178	.012	.252	.212	.250	3
4	.20431	.238	.2253	.0188	.013	.232	.207	.234375	4
5	.18194	.220	.2070	.0202	.014	.212	.204	.21875	5
6	.16202	.203	.1920	.0215	.016	.192	.201	.203125	6
7	.14428	.180	.1770	.023	.018	.176	.199	.1875	7
8	.12849	.165	.1620	.0243	.020	.160	.197	.171875	8
9	.11443	.148	.1483	.0256	.022	.144	.194	.15625	9
10	.10189	.134	.1350	.027	.024	.128	.191	.140625	10
11	.090742	.120	.1205	.0284	.026	.116	.188	.125	11
12	.080808	.109	.1055	.0296	.029	.104	.185	.109375	12
13	.071961	.095	.0915	.0314	.031	.092	.182	.09375	13
14	.064084	.083	.0800	.0326	.033	.080	.180	.078125	14
15	.057068	.072	.0720	.0345	.035	.072	.178	.0703125	15
16	.05082	.065	.0625	.036	.037	.064	.175	.0625	16
17	.045257	.058	.0540	.0377	.039	.056	.172	.05625	17
18	.040303	.049	.0475	.0395	.041	.048	.168	.050	18
19	.03589	.042	.0410	.0414	.043	.040	.164	.04375	19
20	.031961	.035	.0348	.0434	.045	.036	.161	.0375	20
21	.028462	.032	.03175	.046	.047	.032	.157	.034375	21
22	.025347	.028	.0286	.0483	.049	.028	.155	.03125	22
23	.022571	.025	.0258	.051	.051	.024	.153	.028125	23
24	.0201	.022	.0230	.055	.055	.022	.151	.025	24
25	.0179	.020	.0204	.0586	.059	.020	.148	.021875	25
26	.01594	.018	.0181	.0626	.063	.018	.146	.01875	26
27	.014195	.016	.0173	.0658	.067	.0164	.143	.0171875	27
28	.012641	.014	.0162	.072	.071	.0149	.139	.015625	28
29	.011257	.013	.0150	.076	.075	.0136	.134	.0140625	29
30	.010025	.012	.0140	.080	.080	.0124	.127	.0125	30
31	.008928	.010	.0132	....	.085	.0116	.120	.0109375	31
32	.00795	.009	.0128	....	.090	.0108	.115	.01015625	32
33	.00708	.008	.0118	....	.095	.0100	.112	.009375	33
34	.006304	.007	.0104	....	....	.0092	.110	.00889375	34
35	.005614	.005	.0095	....	....	.0084	.108	.0078125	35
36	.005	.004	.0090	....	....	.0076	.106	.00703125	36
37	.004453	....	....	....	....	.0068	.103	.006640625	37
38	.003965	....	....	....	....	.0060	.101	.00625	38
39	.003531	....	....	....	....	.0052	.099	....	39
40	.003144	....	....	....	....	.0048	.097	....	40

TABLE 17

HARDNESS CONVERSION TABLE

C. 150 Kg "Brale" "ROCKWELL"	A. 60 Kg "Brale" "ROCKWELL"	15-N 15 Kg N "Brale" "ROCKWELL" Superficial	30-N 30 Kg N "Brale" "ROCKWELL" Superficial	Pyramid 136° Dia-mond 136° Diamond Pyramid	Br'l 3000 Kg 10 mm Ball Brinell (Hultgren) Ball	Tensile Strength Thousand Lbs. per sq. in.
70	86.5	94.0	86.0	1076	—	
69	86.0	93.5	85.0	1004	—	
68	85.5	—	84.5	942	—	
67	85.0	93.0	83.5	894	—	
66	84.5	92.5	83.0	854	—	
65	84.0	92.0	82.0	820	—	
64	83.5	—	81.0	789	—	
63	83.0	91.5	80.0	763	—	
62	82.5	91.0	79.0	739	—	
61	81.5	90.5	78.5	716	—	
60	81.0	90.0	77.5	695	614	314
59	80.5	89.5	76.5	675	600	306
58	80.0	—	75.5	655	587	299
57	79.5	89.0	75.0	636	573	291
56	79.0	88.5	74.0	617	560	284
55	78.5	88.0	73.0	598	547	277
54	78.0	87.5	72.0	580	534	270
53	77.5	87.0	71.0	562	522	263
52	77.0	86.5	70.5	545	509	256
51	76.5	86.0	69.5	528	496	250
50	76.0	85.5	68.5	513	484	243
49	75.5	85.0	67.5	498	472	236
48	74.5	84.5	66.5	485	460	230
47	74.0	84.0	66.0	471	448	223
46	73.5	83.5	65.0	458	437	217
45	73.0	83.0	64.0	446	426	211
44	72.5	82.5	63.0	435	415	205
42	71.5	81.5	61.5	413	393	194
40	70.5	80.5	59.5	393	372	182
38	69.5	79.5	57.5	373	352	171
36	68.5	78.5	56.0	353	332	162
34	67.5	77.0	54.0	334	313	153
32	66.5	76.0	52.0	317	297	144
30	65.5	75.0	50.5	301	263	136
28	64.5	74.0	48.5	285	270	129
26	63.5	72.5	47.0	271	260	123
24	62.5	71.5	45.0	257	250	117
22	61.5	70.5	43.0	246	240	112
20	60.5	69.5	41.5	236	230	108

INEXACT AND ONLY FOR STEEL

TABLE 17—Continued

HARDNESS CONVERSION TABLE

B. 100 Kg 1/16" Ball "ROCKWELL"	F. 60 Kg 1/16" Ball "ROCKWELL"	15-T 15 Kg 1/16" Ball "ROCKWELL" Superficial	30-T 30 Kg 1/16" Ball "ROCKWELL" Superficial	Br'l 3000 Kg 10 mm Ball Brinell	Tensile Strength Thousand Lbs. per sq. in.
100	—	93.0	82.0	240	116
99	—	92.5	81.5	234	112
98	—	—	81.0	228	109
97	—	92.0	80.5	222	106
96	—	—	80.0	216	103
95	—	91.5	79.0	210	101
94	—	—	78.5	205	98
93	—	91.0	78.0	200	96
92	—	90.5	77.5	195	93
91	—	—	77.0	190	91
90	—	90.0	76.0	185	89
89	—	89.5	75.5	180	87
88	—	—	75.0	176	85
87	—	89.0	74.5	172	83
86	—	88.5	74.0	169	81
85	—	—	73.5	165	80
84	—	88.0	73.0	162	78
83	—	87.5	72.0	159	77
82	—	—	71.5	156	75
81	—	87.0	71.0	153	74
80	—	86.5	70.0	150	72
79	—	—	69.5	147	
78	—	86.0	69.0	144	
77	—	85.5	68.0	141	
76	—	—	67.5	139	
75	99.5	85.0	67.0	137	
74	99.0	—	66.0	135	
72	98.0	84.0	65.0	130	
70	97.0	83.5	63.5	125	
68	95.5	83.0	62.0	121	
66	94.5	82.0	60.5	117	
64	93.5	81.5	59.5	114	
62	92.0	80.5	58.0	110	
60	91.0	80.0	56.5	107	
58	90.0	79.5	55.0	104	
56	89.0	79.0	54.0	101	
54	87.5	78.0	52.5	*87	
52	86.5	77.5	51.0	*85	
50	85.5	77.0	49.5	*83	
48	84.5	76.0	48.5	*81	
46	83.0	75.5	47.0	*79	
44	82.0	75.0	45.5	*78	
42	81.0	74.0	44.0	*76	
40	79.5	73.5	43.0	*74	
38	78.5	73.0	41.5	*73	
36	77.5	72.0	40.0	*71	
34	76.5	71.5	38.5	*70	
32	75.0	71.0	37.5	*68	
30	74.0	70.5	36.0	*67	
28	73.0	69.5	34.5	*66	
24	70.5	68.5	32.0	*64	
20	68.5	67.0	29.0	*62	
16	66.0	66.0	26.0	*60	
12	64.0	64.5	23.5	*58	
8	61.5	63.5	20.5	*56	
4	59.5	62.0	18.0	*55	
0	57.0	61.0	15.0	*53	

The 15N, 30N, 15T and 30T Scales pertain to our "ROCKWELL" Superficial Hardness Testers which apply exceedingly light minor and major loads for very shallow indentations, as required for testing nitrided steel or thin sheet metal.

All relatives values on this card are averages of tests on various metals whose differences in cold-working and other properties prevent establishment of exact mathematical conversion. Hardness values here given were carefully determined in our own Standard Laboratory.

COPYRIGHT 1939 BY WILSON MECHANICAL INSTRUMENT CO., INC.

Even for steel, Tensile Strength relation to hardness is inexact, unless determined for specific material.

WILSON

RELATIONSHIP TABLE 38

* Below Brinell 101 tests were made with only 500 kg load and 10mm ball.

179

Appendix

TABLE 18

SCREW THREADS AND TAP DRILL SIZES

N C or A.S.M.E. SPECIAL MACHINE SCREWS

Size of Tap	Thds. per Inch	Tap Drill	Body Drill
1	64	53	47
2	56	50	42
3	48	47	37
4	40	43	31
5	40	38	29
6	32	36	27
8	32	29	18
10	24	25	9
12	24	16	2

N F or A.S.M.E. STANDARD MACHINE SCREWS

Size of Tap	Thds. per Inch	Tap Drill	Body Drill
2	64	50	42
3	56	45	37
4	48	42	31
5	44	37	29
6	40	33	27
8	36	29	18
10	32	21	9
*10	30	22	9
12	28	14	2

*A.S.M.E. only

N P T PIPE THREADS

Size of Tap	Thds. per Inch	Tap Drill
$\frac{1}{8}$	27	R
$\frac{1}{4}$	18	$\frac{7}{16}$
$\frac{3}{8}$	18	$\frac{37}{64}$
$\frac{1}{2}$	14	$\frac{23}{32}$
$\frac{3}{4}$	14	$\frac{59}{64}$
1	$11\frac{1}{2}$	$1\frac{5}{32}$
$1\frac{1}{4}$	$11\frac{1}{2}$	$1\frac{1}{2}$
$1\frac{1}{2}$	$11\frac{1}{2}$	$1\frac{47}{64}$
2	$11\frac{1}{2}$	$2\frac{7}{32}$
$2\frac{1}{2}$	8	$2\frac{5}{8}$
3	8	$3\frac{1}{4}$

N F or S.A.E. STANDARD SCREWS

Size of Tap	Thds. per Inch	Tap Drill
$\frac{1}{4}$	28	3
$\frac{5}{16}$	24	I
$\frac{3}{8}$	24	Q
$\frac{7}{16}$	20	$\frac{25}{64}$
$\frac{1}{2}$	20	$\frac{29}{64}$
$\frac{9}{16}$	18	$\frac{33}{64}$
$\frac{5}{8}$	18	$\frac{37}{64}$
*$\frac{11}{16}$	16	$\frac{5}{8}$
$\frac{3}{4}$	16	$\frac{11}{16}$
$\frac{7}{8}$	14	$\frac{13}{16}$
1	14	$\frac{15}{16}$
$1\frac{1}{8}$	12	$1\frac{3}{64}$

*S.A.E. only

**Tap Drills allow approx. 75% Full Thread
N.P.T. = American National Taper Pipe Thread**

TABLE 19

DRILL SIZES

SIZE	DECIMAL EQUIV.	SIZE	DECIMAL EQUIV.	SIZE	DECIMAL EQUIV.	SIZE	DECIMAL EQUIV.
1/2	.5000	G	.2610	23	.1540	1/16	.0625
31/64	.4844	F	.2570	24	.1520	53	.0595
15/32	.4687	E 1/4	.2500	25	.1495	54	.055
29/64	.4531	D	.2460	26	.1470	55	.0520
7/16	.4375	C	.2420	27	.1440	3/64	.0469
27/64	.4219	B	.2380	9/64	.1406	56	.0465
Z	.4130	15/64	.2344	28	.1405	57	.0430
13/32	.4062	A	.2340	29	.1360	58	.0420
Y	.4040	1	.2280	30	.1285	59	.0410
X	.3970	2	.2210	1/8	.1250	60	.0400
25/64	.3906	7/32	.2187	31	.1200	61	.0390
W	.3860	3	.2130	32	.1160	62	.0380
V	.3770	4	.2090	33	.1130	63	.0370
3/8	.3750	5	.2055	34	.1110	64	.0360
U	.3680	6	.2040	35	.1100	65	.0350
23/64	.3594	13/64	.2031	7/64	.1094	66	.0330
T	.3580	7	.2010	36	.1065	67	.0320
S	.3480	8	.1990	37	.1040	1/32	.0313
11/32	.3437	9	.1960	38	.1015	68	.0310
R	.3390	10	.1935	39	.0995	69	.0292
Q	.3320	11	.1910	40	.0980	70	.0280
21/64	.3281	12	.1890	41	.0960	71	.0260
P	.3230	3/16	.1875	3/32	.0937	72	.0250
O	.3160	13	.1850	42	.0935	73	.0240
5/16	.3125	14	.1820	43	.0890	74	.0225
N	.3020	15	.1800	44	.0860	75	.0210
19/64	.2969	16	.1770	45	.0820	76	.0200
M	.2950	17	.1730	46	.0810	77	.0180
L	.2900	11/64	.1719	47	.0785	78	.0160
9/32	.2812	18	.1695	5/64	.0781	1/64	.0156
K	.2810	19	.1660	48	.0760	79	.0145
J	.2770	20	.1610	49	.0730	80	.0135
I	.2720	21	.1590	50	.0700		
H	.2660	22	.1570	51	.0670		
17/64	.2656	5/32	.1562	52	.0635		

Appendix

TABLE 20

CHEMICAL ELEMENTS AND SYMBOLS

Chemical Element	Symbol	Specific Gravity
Aluminum	Al	2.70
Antimony	Sb	6.62
Argon	A	1.380
Arsenic	As	4.8
Barium	Ba	3.78
Beryllium	Be	1.84
Bismuth	Bi	9.75
Boron	B	2.45
Bromine	Br	3.188
Cadmium	Cd	8.6
Caesium	Cs	1.88
Calcium	Ca	1.55
Carbon	C	1.9–3.52
Cerium	Ce	6.92
Chlorine	Cl	1.408
Chromium	Cr	6.92
Cobalt	Co	8.756
Copper	Cu	8.91
Erbium	Er	4.77
Fluorine	F	1.31
Gadolinium	Gd	.....
Gallium	Ga	5.89
Germanium	Ge	5.47
Glucinum	Gl	1.84
Gold	Au	19.32
Helium	He	0.1368
Hydrogen	H	0.0695
Indium	In	7.36
Iodine	I	4.94
Iridium	Ir	22.42
Iron	Fe	7.85
Krypton	Kr	2.87
Lanthanum	La	6.154
Lead	Pb	11.38
Lithium	Li	0.59
Magnesium	Mg	1.74
Manganese	Mn	7.42
Mercury	Hg	13.596
Molybdenum	Mo	10.2
Neodymium	Nd	6.96

TABLE 20—*Continued*

CHEMICAL ELEMENTS AND SYMBOLS

Chemical Element	Symbol	Specific Gravity
Neon	Ne	0.674
Nickel	Ni	8.84
Niobium or Columbium	Nb or CB	8.4
Nitrogen	N	0.967
Osmíum	Os	22.48
Oxygen	O	1.1056
Palladium	Pd	12.16
Phosphorus	P	1.83
Platinum	Pt	21.40
Potassium	K	0.862
Praesodymium	Pr	6.48
Radium	Ra	. . . . .
Rhodium	Rh	12.44
Rubidium	Rb	1.52
Ruthenium	Ru	12.1
Samarium	Sm	7.7
Scandium	Sc	. . . . .
Selenium	Se	4.26
Silicon	Si	2.35
Silver	Ag	10.7
Sodium	Na	0.971
Strontium	Sr	2.54
Sulphur	S	2.05–2.09
Tantalum	Ta	16.6
Tellurium	Te	6.2
Terbium	Tb	. . . . .
Thallium	Tl	11.86
Thorium	Th	11.3
Thulium	Tm	. . . . .
Tin	Sn	7.298
Titanium	Ti	. . . . .
Tungsten	W	19.6
Uranium	U	18.68
Vanadium	V	6.02
Xenon	Xe	4.53
Ytterbium	Yb	. . . . .
Yttrium	Yt	3.80
Zerconium	Zn	7.142
Zinc	Zr	. . . . .

TABLE 21
CONVERSION FACTORS

LENGTH			VOLUME	
UNIT	VALUE IN OTHER UNITS		UNIT	VALUE IN OTHER UNITS
1 inch	1000 mils 2.54 centimeters 25.4 millimeters 11.25 lignes		1 Cubic Inch	16.39 cubic centimeters
			1 Cubic Foot	1728 Cubic Inches 7.4805 gallons (U.S.) 28.32 liters
.0888 in.	1 ligne			
.001 "	1 mil		1.245 " Feet	1 bushel dry measure
.03937 "	1 millimeter		1 Cubic Yard	27 Cubic feet
0.3937 "	1 centimeter		1 Cubic Centi- meter	.061 cubic inches
39.37 "	1 meter (3.28 feet)		1 Liter	61.023 cubic inches 1.0567 quarts .2642 gallons (U.S.) .2196 gallons (English measure)
1 Yard	.9144 meters			
1 Mile	5280 feet 1760 yards .868 knots (nautical miles) 1.609 kilometers		.9463 Liters	1 quart
			3.7854 Liters	1 gallon (U.S.)
.6214 miles	1 kilometer		1 pint	4 gills
1 Knot (nautical mile)	6080.26 feet 1.151 miles		2 Pints	1 quart
			1 Gallon	4 quarts 8 pints 231 cubic inches (U.S. measure) 277.27 cubic inches (English measure) .1335 cubic feet 3.7854 liters .831 gallons (English measure)
Board Feet	Length in feet x width in feet x thickness in inches			
1 Millimeter	.4430 ligne .03937 inches			
.001 "	1 micron			
2.25 "	1 ligne			
1 Centimeter	.3937 inches		1.2032 Gallons (U.S.)	1 gallon (English meas- ure)
1 Meter	39.37 inches 3.281 feet			
.9144 Meters	1 yard			

TABLE 21—*Continued*

CONVERSION FACTORS

Unit	Value in Other Units	Unit	Value in Other Units
Weight		**Weight**	
Avoirdupois		*English-Metric Weight Conversion Factor*	
1 Ounce	437.5 grains (Same grain as Troy) 28.35 grams .0625 pounds (1/16) .9115 ounces Troy	1 Grain	64.80 Milligrams .0648 grams
		.0154 Grains	1 Milligram
		15.432 Grains	1 Gram
.0353 Ounces	1 grain	1 Pound (Avoir.)	.4536 Kilograms
16 Ounces	1 pound = 7000 grains		
1 Short Ton	2000 pounds	2.2046 Pounds (Avoir.)	1 Kilogram
1 Long Ton	2240 pounds	*Miscellaneous*	
1 Pound	1.215 pounds Troy		
		1 Minute	60 Seconds
Troy		60 Minutes	1 Degree
1 Ounce	480 grains (same grain as Avoirdupois) 20 pennyweight (1 pennyweight = 24 grains) 31.10 grams .0833 pounds (1/12) 1.097 ounces Avoirdupois	1 B.T.U. (British Thermal Unit)	252 Calories
		1 Calorie	.003968 B.T.U.
		1 Inch Ounce	720.09 Millimeter Grams
.03215 Ounces	1 gram	1 Horsepower Hour	.7452 Kilowatt Hours
12 Ounces	1 pound = 5760 grains		
1 Carat	3.168 grains 205 Milligrams 200 Milligrams (International carat)	1 Horsepower	745.2 watts 33,000 foot pounds per minute 550 foot pounds per second 2545 B.T.U. per hour
1 Pound	.823 Pounds Avoirdupois	1 Kilowatt	1.34 Horsepower
Dry		1 Kilowatt Hour	1000 Watt hours 1.34 Horsepower hours 3412 B.T.U.
1 Quart	2 Pints		
8 Quarts	1 peck	π Radians	180 Degrees
1 Bushel	4 pecks	1 Radian	57.2958 Degrees

TABLE 22

DECIMAL EQUIVALENTS OF FRACTIONS OF AN INCH

| Fraction |||||| Decimal |
4ths	8ths	16ths	32nds	64ths	Equivalent
				1/64	0.015 625
			1/32		0.031 25
				3/64	0.046 875
		1/16			0.062 5
				5/64	0.078 125
			3/32		0.093 75
				7/64	0.109 375
	1/8				0.125
				9/64	0.140 625
			5/32		0.156 25
				11/64	0.171 875
		3/16			0.187 5
				13/64	0.203 125
			7/32		0.218 75
				15/64	0.234 375
1/4					0.250
				17/64	0.265 625
			9/32		0.281 25
				19/64	0.296 875
		5/16			0.312 5
				21/64	0.328 125

| Fraction |||||| Decimal |
4ths	8ths	16ths	32nds	64ths	Equivalent
			11/32		0.343 75
				23/64	0.359 375
	3/8				0.375
				25/64	0.390 625
			13/32		0.406 25
				27/64	0.421 875
		7/16			0.437 5
				29/64	0.453 125
			15/32		0.468 75
				31/64	0.484 375
1/2					0.500
				33/64	0.515 625
			17/32		0.531 25
				35/64	0.546 875
		9/16			0.562 5
				37/64	0.578 125
			19/32		0.593 75
				39/64	0.609 375
	5/8				0.625
				41/64	0.640 625
			21/32		0.656 25

| Fraction |||||| Decimal |
4ths	8ths	16ths	32nds	64ths	Equivalent
				43/64	0.671 875
		11/16			0.687 5
				45/64	0.703 125
			23/32		0.718 75
				47/64	0.734 375
3/4					0.750
				49/64	0.765 625
			25/32		0.781 25
				51/64	0.796 875
		13/16			0.812 5
				53/64	0.828 125
			27/32		0.843 75
				55/64	0.859 375
	7/8				0.875
				57/64	0.890 625
			29/32		0.906 25
				59/64	0.921 875
		15/16			0.937 5
				61/64	0.953 125
			31/32		0.968 75
				63/64	0.984 375

TABLE 23

RULES RELATIVE TO THE CIRCLE, ETC.

To Find Circumference—
Multiply diameter by   3.1416   Or divide diameter by   0.3183

To Find Diameter—
Multiply circumference by   0.3183   Or divide circumference by 3.1416

To Find Radius—
Multiply circumference by   0.15915 Or divide circumference by 6.28318

To Find Side of an Inscribed Square—
Multiply diameter by   0.7071
Or multiply circumference by 0.2251   Or divide circumference by 4.4428

To Find Side of an Equal Square—
Multiply diameter by   0.8862   Or divide diameter by   1.1284
Or multiply circumference by 0.2821   Or divide circumference by 3.545

Square—
A side multiplied by   1.4142 equals diameter of its circumscribing circle.
A side multiplied by   4.443   equals circumference of its circumscribing circle.
A side multiplied by   1.128   equals diameter of an equal circle.
A side multiplied by   3.547   equals circumference of an equal circle.
Square inches multiplied by   1.273   equal circle inches of an equal circle.

To Find the Area of a Circle—
Multiply circumference by one-quarter of the diameter.
Or multiply the square of diameter by   0.7854
Or multiply the square of circumference by   .07958
Or multiply the square of ½ diameter by   3.1416

To Find the Surface of a Sphere or Globe—
Multiply the diameter by the circumference.
Or multiply the square of diameter by   3.1416
Or multiply four times the square of radius by 3.1416

To Find the Weight of Brass and Copper Sheets, Rods and Bars—
Ascertain the number of cubic inches in piece and multiply same by weight per cubic inch.
Brass,   0.2972
Copper, 0.3212
Or multiply the length by the breadth (in feet) and product by weight in pounds per square foot.

TABLE 24

FUNCTIONS OF NUMBERS, 1 TO 49

No.	Square	Cube	Square Root	Cubic Root	Logarithm	1000 x Reciprocal	No. = Diameter Circum.	No. = Diameter Area
1	1	1	1.0000	1.0000	0.00000	1000.000	3.142	0.7854
2	4	8	1.4142	1.2599	0.30103	500.000	6.283	3.1416
3	9	27	1.7321	1.4422	0.47712	333.333	9.425	7.0686
4	16	64	2.0000	1.5874	0.60206	250.000	12.566	12.5664
5	25	125	2.2361	1.7100	0.69897	200.000	15.708	19.6350
6	36	216	2.4495	1.8171	0.77815	166.667	18.850	28.2743
7	49	343	2.6458	1.9129	0.84510	142.857	21.991	38.4845
8	64	512	2.8284	2.0000	0.90309	125.000	25.133	50.2655
9	81	729	3.0000	2.0801	0.95424	111.111	28.274	63.6173
10	100	1000	3.1623	2.1544	1.00000	100.000	31.416	78.5398
11	121	1331	3.3166	2.2240	1.04139	90.9091	34.558	95.0332
12	144	1728	3.4641	2.2894	1.07918	83.3333	37.699	113.097
13	169	2197	3.6056	2.3513	1.11394	76.9231	40.841	132.732
14	196	2744	3.7417	2.4101	1.14613	71.4286	43.982	153.938
15	225	3375	3.8730	2.4662	1.17609	66.6667	47.124	176.715
16	256	4096	4.0000	2.5198	1.20412	62.5000	50.265	201.062
17	289	4913	4.1231	2.5713	1.23045	58.8235	53.407	226.980
18	324	5832	4.2426	2.6207	1.25527	55.5556	56.549	254.469
19	361	6859	4.3589	2.6684	1.27875	52.6316	59.690	283.529
20	400	8000	4.4721	2.7144	1.30103	50.0000	62.832	314.159
21	441	9261	4.5826	2.7589	1.32222	47.6190	65.973	346.361
22	484	10648	4.6904	2.8020	1.34242	45.4545	69.115	380.133
23	529	12167	4.7958	2.8439	1.36173	43.4783	72.257	415.476
24	576	13824	4.8990	2.8845	1.38021	41.6667	75.398	452.389
25	625	15625	5.0000	2.9240	1.39794	40.0000	78.540	490.874
26	676	17576	5.0990	2.9625	1.41497	38.4615	81.681	530.929
27	729	19683	5.1962	3.0000	1.43136	37.0370	84.823	572.555
28	784	21952	5.2915	3.0366	1.44716	35.7143	87.965	615.752
29	841	24389	5.3852	3.0723	1.46240	34.4828	91.106	660.520
30	900	27000	5.4772	3.1072	1.47712	33.3333	94.248	706.858
31	961	29791	5.5678	3.1414	1.49136	32.2581	97.389	754.768
32	1024	32768	5.6569	3.1748	1.50515	31.2500	100.531	804.248
33	1089	35937	5.7446	3.2075	1.51851	30.3030	103.673	855.299
34	1156	39304	5.8310	3.2396	1.53148	29.4118	106.814	907.920
35	1225	42875	5.9161	3.2711	1.54407	28.5714	109.956	962.113
36	1296	46656	6.0000	3.3019	1.55630	27.7778	113.097	1017.88
37	1369	50653	6.0828	3.3322	1.56820	27.0270	116.239	1075.21
38	1444	54872	6.1644	3.3620	1.57978	26.3158	119.381	1134.11
39	1521	59319	6.2450	3.3912	1.59106	25.6410	122.522	1194.59
40	1600	64000	6.3246	3.4200	1.60206	25.0000	125.66	1256.64
41	1681	68921	6.4031	3.4482	1.61278	24.3902	128.81	1320.25
42	1764	74088	6.4807	3.4760	1.62325	23.8095	131.95	1385.44
43	1849	79507	6.5574	3.5034	1.63347	23.2558	135.09	1452.20
44	1936	85184	6.6332	3.5303	1.64345	22.7273	138.23	1520.53
45	2025	91125	6.7082	3.5569	1.65321	22.2222	141.37	1590.43
46	2116	97336	6.7823	3.5830	1.66276	21.7391	144.51	1661.90
47	2209	103823	6.8557	3.6088	1.67210	21.2766	147.65	1734.94
48	2304	110592	6.9282	3.6342	1.68124	20.8333	150.80	1809.56
49	2401	117649	7.0000	3.6593	1.69020	20.4082	153.94	1885.74

188

TABLE 24—*Continued*

FUNCTIONS OF NUMBERS, 50 TO 99

No.	Square	Cube	Square Root	Cubic Root	Logarithm	1000 x Reciprocal	No. = Diameter Circum.	Area
50	2500	125000	7.0711	3.6840	1.69897	20.0000	157.08	1963.50
51	2601	132651	7.1414	3.7084	1.70757	19.6078	160.22	2042.82
52	2704	140608	7.2111	3.7325	1.71600	19.2308	163.36	2123.72
53	2809	148877	7.2801	3.7563	1.72428	18.8679	166.50	2206.18
54	2916	157464	7.3485	3.7798	1.73239	18.5185	169.65	2290.22
55	3025	166375	7.4162	3.8030	1.74036	18.1818	172.79	2375.83
56	3136	175616	7.4833	3.8259	1.74819	17.8571	175.93	2463.01
57	3249	185193	7.5498	3.8485	1.75587	17.5439	179.07	2551.76
58	3364	195112	7.6158	3.8709	1.76343	17.2414	182.21	2642.08
59	3481	205379	7.6811	3.8930	1.77085	16.9492	185.35	2733.97
60	3600	216000	7.7460	3.9149	1.77815	16.6667	188.50	2827.43
61	3721	226981	7.8102	3.9365	1.78533	16.3934	191.64	2922.47
62	3844	238328	7.8740	3.9579	1.79239	16.1290	194.78	3019.07
63	3969	250047	7.9373	3.9791	1.79934	15.8730	197.92	3117.25
64	4096	262144	8.0000	4.0000	1.80618	15.6250	201.06	3216.99
65	4225	274625	8.0623	4.0207	1.81291	15.3846	204.20	3318.31
66	4356	287496	8.1240	4.0412	1.81954	15.1515	207.35	3421.19
67	4489	300763	8.1854	4.0615	1.82607	14.9254	210.49	3525.65
68	4624	314432	8.2462	4.0817	1.83251	14.7059	213.63	3631.68
69	4761	328509	8.3006	4.1016	1.83885	14.4928	216.77	3739.28
70	4900	343000	8.3666	4.1213	1.84510	14.2857	219.91	3848.45
71	5041	357911	8.4261	4.1408	1.85126	14.0845	223.05	3959.19
72	5184	373248	8.4853	4.1602	1.85733	13.8889	226.19	4071.50
73	5329	389017	8.5440	4.1793	1.86332	13.6986	229.34	4185.39
74	5476	405224	8.6023	4.1983	1.86923	13.5135	232.48	4300.84
75	5625	421875	8.6603	4.2172	1.87506	13.3333	235.62	4417.86
76	5776	438976	8.7178	4.2358	1.88081	13.1579	238.76	4536.46
77	5929	456533	8.7750	4.2543	1.88649	12.9870	241.90	4656.63
78	6084	474552	8.8318	4.2727	1.89209	12.8205	245.04	4778.36
79	6241	493039	8.8882	4.2908	1.89763	12.6582	248.19	4901.67
80	6400	512000	8.9443	4.3089	1.90309	12.5000	251.33	5026.55
81	6561	531441	9.0000	4.3267	1.90849	12.3457	254.47	5153.00
82	6724	551368	9.0554	4.3445	1.91381	12.1951	257.61	5281.02
83	6889	571787	9.1104	4.3621	1.91908	12.0482	260.75	5410.61
84	7056	592704	9.1652	4.3795	1.92428	11.9048	263.89	5541.77
85	7225	614125	9.2195	4.3968	1.92942	11.7647	267.04	5674.50
86	7396	636056	9.2736	4.4140	1.93450	11.6279	270.18	5808.80
87	7569	658503	9.3274	4.4310	1.93952	11.4943	273.32	5944.68
88	7744	681472	9.3808	4.4480	1.94448	11.3636	276.46	6082.12
89	7921	704969	9.4340	4.4647	1.94939	11.2360	279.60	6221.14
90	8100	729000	9.4868	4.4814	1.95424	11.1111	282.74	6361.73
91	8281	753571	9.5394	4.4979	1.95904	10.9890	285.88	6503.88
92	8464	778688	9.5917	4.5144	1.96379	10.8696	289.03	6647.61
93	8649	804357	9.6437	4.5307	1.96848	10.7527	292.17	6792.91
94	8836	830584	9.6954	4.5468	1.97313	10.6383	295.31	6939.78
95	9025	857375	9.7468	4.5629	1.97772	10.5263	298.45	7088.22
96	9216	884736	9.7980	4.5789	1.98227	10.4167	301.59	7238.23
97	9409	912673	9.8489	4.5947	1.98677	10.3093	304.73	7389.81
98	9604	941192	9.8995	4.6104	1.99123	10.2041	307.88	7542.96
99	9801	970299	9.9499	4.6261	1.99564	10.1010	311.02	7697.69

TABLE 24—Continued

FUNCTIONS OF NUMBERS, 100 TO 149

No.	Square	Cube	Square Root	Cubic Root	Logarithm	1000 x Reciprocal	No. = Diameter Circum.	Area
100	10000	1000000	10.0000	4.6416	2.00000	10.0000	314.16	7853.98
101	10201	1030301	10.0499	4.6570	2.00432	9.90099	317.30	8011.85
102	10404	1061208	10.0995	4.6723	2.00860	9.80392	320.44	8171.28
103	10609	1092727	10.1489	4.6875	2.01284	9.70874	323.58	8332.29
104	10816	1124864	10.1980	4.7027	2.01703	9.61538	326.73	8494.87
105	11025	1157625	10.2470	4.7177	2.02119	9.52381	329.87	8659.01
106	11236	1191016	10.2956	4.7326	2.02531	9.43396	333.01	8824.73
107	11449	1225043	10.3441	4.7475	2.02938	9.34579	336.15	8992.02
108	11664	1259712	10.3923	4.7622	2.03342	9.25926	339.29	9160.88
109	11881	1295029	10.4403	4.7769	2.03743	9.17431	342.43	9331.32
110	12100	1331000	10.4881	4.7914	2.04139	9.09091	345.58	9503.32
111	12321	1367631	10.5357	4.8059	2.04532	9.00901	348.72	9676.89
112	12544	1404928	10.5830	4.8203	2.04922	8.92857	351.86	9852.03
113	12769	1442897	10.6301	4.8346	2.05308	8.84956	355.00	10028.7
114	12996	1481544	10.6771	4.8488	2.05690	8.77193	358.14	10207.0
115	13225	1520875	10.7238	4.8629	2.06070	8.69565	361.28	10386.9
116	13456	1560896	10.7703	4.8770	2.06446	8.62069	364.42	10568.3
117	13689	1601613	10.8167	4.8910	2.06819	8.54701	367.57	10751.3
118	13924	1643032	10.8628	4.9049	2.07188	8.47458	370.71	10935.9
119	14161	1685159	10.9087	4.9187	2.07555	8.40336	373.85	11122.0
120	14400	1728000	10.9545	4.9324	2.07918	8.33333	376.99	11309.7
121	14641	1771561	11.0000	4.9461	2.08279	8.26446	380.13	11499.0
122	14884	1815848	11.0454	4.9597	2.08636	8.19672	383.27	11689.9
123	15129	1860867	11.0905	4.9732	2.08991	8.13008	386.42	11882.3
124	15376	1906624	11.1355	4.9866	2.09342	8.06452	389.56	12076.3
125	15625	1953125	11.1803	5.0000	2.09691	8.00000	392.70	12271.8
126	15876	2000376	11.2250	5.0133	2.10037	7.93651	395.84	12469.0
127	16129	2048383	11.2694	5.0265	2.10380	7.87402	398.98	12667.7
128	16384	2097152	11.3137	5.0397	2.10721	7.81250	402.12	12868.0
129	16641	2146689	11.3578	5.0528	2.11059	7.75194	405.27	13069.8
130	16900	2197000	11.4018	5.0658	2.11394	7.69231	408.41	13273.2
131	17161	2248091	11.4455	5.0788	2.11727	7.63359	411.55	13478.2
132	17424	2299968	11.4891	5.0916	2.12057	7.57576	414.69	13684.8
133	17689	2352637	11.5326	5.1045	2.12385	7.51880	417.83	13892.9
134	17956	2406104	11.5758	5.1172	2.12710	7.46269	420.97	14102.6
135	18225	2460375	11.6190	5.1299	2.13033	7.40741	424.12	14313.9
136	18496	2515456	11.6619	5.1426	2.13354	7.35294	427.26	14526.7
137	18769	2571353	11.7047	5.1551	2.13672	7.29927	430.40	14741.1
138	19044	2628072	11.7473	5.1676	2.13988	7.24638	433.54	14957.1
139	19321	2685619	11.7898	5.1801	2.14301	7.19424	436.68	15174.7
140	19600	2744000	11.8322	5.1925	2.14613	7.14286	439.82	15393.8
141	19881	2803221	11.8743	5.2048	2.14922	7.09220	442.96	15614.5
142	20164	2863288	11.9164	5.2171	2.15229	7.04225	446.11	15836.8
143	20449	2924207	11.9583	5.2293	2.15534	6.99301	449.25	16060.6
144	20736	2985984	12.0000	5.2415	2.15836	6.94444	452.39	16286.0
145	21025	3048625	12.0416	5.2536	2.16137	6.89655	455.53	16513.0
146	21316	3112136	12.0830	5.2656	2.16435	6.84932	458.67	16741.5
147	21609	3176523	12.1244	5.2776	2.16732	6.80272	461.81	16971.7
148	21904	3241792	12.1655	5.2896	2.17026	6.75676	464.96	17203.4
149	22201	3307949	12.2066	5.3015	2.17319	6.71141	468.10	17436.6

TABLE 24—*Continued*

FUNCTIONS OF NUMBERS, 150 TO 199

No.	Square	Cube	Square Root	Cubic Root	Logarithm	1000 x Reciprocal	No. = Diameter Circum.	Area
150	22500	3375000	12.2474	5.3133	2.17609	6.66667	471.24	17671.5
151	22801	3442951	12.2882	5.3251	2.17898	6.62252	474.38	17907.9
152	23104	3511808	12.3288	5.3368	2.18184	6.57895	477.52	18145.8
153	23409	3581577	12.3693	5.3485	2.18469	6.53595	480.66	18385.4
154	23716	3652264	12.4097	5.3601	2.18752	6.49351	483.81	18626.5
155	24025	3723875	12.4499	5.3717	2.19033	6.45161	486.95	18869.2
156	24336	3796416	12.4900	5.3832	2.19312	6.41026	490.09	19113 4
157	24649	3869893	12.5300	5.3947	2.19590	6.36943	493.23	19359.3
158	24964	3944312	12.5698	5.4061	2.19866	6.32911	496.37	19606.7
159	25281	4019679	12.6095	5.4175	2.20140	6.28931	499.51	19855.7
160	25600	4096000	12.6491	5.4288	2.20412	6.25000	502.65	20106.2
161	25921	4173281	12.6886	5.4401	2.20683	6.21118	505.80	20358.3
162	26244	4251528	12.7279	5.4514	2.20952	6.17284	508.94	20612.0
163	26569	4330747	12.7671	5.4626	2.21219	6.13497	512.08	20867.2
164	26896	4410944	12.8062	5.4737	2.21484	6.09756	515.22	21124.1
165	27225	4492125	12.8452	5.4848	2.21748	6.06061	518.36	21382.5
166	27556	4574296	12.8841	5.4959	2.22011	6.02410	521.50	21642.4
167	27889	4657463	12.9228	5.5069	2.22272	5.98802	524.65	21904.0
168	28224	4741632	12.9615	5.5178	2.22531	5.95238	527.79	22167.1
169	28561	4826809	13.0000	5.5288	2.22789	5.91716	530.93	22431.8
170	28900	4913000	13.0384	5.5397	2.23045	5.88235	534.07	22698.0
171	29241	5000211	13.0767	5.5505	2.23300	5.84795	537.21	22965.8
172	29584	5088448	13.1149	5.5613	2.23553	5.81395	540.35	23235.2
173	29929	5177717	13.1529	5.5721	2.23805	5.78035	543.50	23506.2
174	30276	5268024	13.1909	5.5828	2.24055	5.74713	546.64	23778.7
175	30625	5359375	13.2288	5.5934	2.24304	5.71429	549.78	24052.8
176	30976	5451776	13.2665	5.6041	2.24551	5.68182	552.92	24328.5
177	31329	5545233	13.3041	5.6147	2.24797	5.64972	556.06	24605.7
178	31684	5639752	13.3417	5.6252	2.25042	5.61798	559.20	24884.6
179	32041	5735339	13.3791	5.6357	2.25285	5.58659	562.35	25164.9
180	32400	5832000	13.4164	5.6462	2.25527	5.55556	565.49	25446.9
181	32761	5929741	13.4536	5.6567	2.25768	5.52486	568.63	25730.4
182	33124	6028568	13.4907	5.6671	2.26007	5.49451	571.77	26015.5
183	33489	6128487	13.5277	5.6774	2.26245	5.46448	574.91	26302.2
184	33856	6229504	13.5647	5.6877	2.26482	5.43478	578.05	26590.4
185	34225	6331625	13.6015	5.6980	2.26717	5.40541	581.19	26880.3
186	34596	6434856	13.6382	5.7083	2.26951	5.37634	584.34	27171.6
187	34969	6539203	13.6748	5.7185	2.27184	5.34759	587.48	27464.6
188	35344	6644672	13.7113	5.7287	2.27416	5.31915	590.62	27759.1
189	35721	6751269	13.7477	5.7388	2.27646	5.29101	593.76	28055.2
190	36100	6859000	13.7840	5.7489	2.27875	5.26316	596.90	28352.9
191	36481	6967871	13.8203	5.7590	2.28103	5.23560	600.04	28652.1
192	36864	7077888	13.8564	5.7690	2.28330	5.20833	603.19	28952.9
193	37249	7189057	13.8924	5.7790	2.28556	5.18135	606.33	29255.3
194	37636	7301384	13.9284	5.7890	2.28780	5.15464	609.47	29559.2
195	38025	7414875	13.9642	5.7989	2.29003	5.12821	612.61	29864.8
196	38416	7529536	14.0000	5.8088	2.29226	5.10204	615.75	30171.9
197	38809	7645373	14.0357	5.8186	2.29447	5.07614	618.89	30480.5
198	39204	7762392	14.0712	5.8285	2.29667	5.05051	622.04	30790.7
199	39601	7880599	14.1067	5.8383	2.29885	5.02513	625.18	31102.6

TABLE 25

TABLE FOR SOLVING RIGHT-ANGLED TRIANGLES

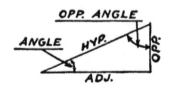

PARTS GIVEN	PARTS TO BE FOUND				
	Hyp.	Adj.	Opp.	Angle	Opp. Angle
Hyp. & Adj.	———	———	$\sqrt{\text{Hyp.}^2\text{-Adj.}^2}$	$\text{Cos.} = \dfrac{\text{Adj.}}{\text{Hyp.}}$	$\text{Sin.} = \dfrac{\text{Adj.}}{\text{Hyp.}}$
Hyp. & Opp.	———	$\sqrt{\text{Hyp.}^2\text{-Opp.}^2}$	———	$\text{Sin.} = \dfrac{\text{Opp.}}{\text{Hyp.}}$	$\text{Cos.} = \dfrac{\text{Opp.}}{\text{Hyp.}}$
Hyp. & Angle	———	Hyp. x Cos.	Hyp. x Sin.	———	90°-Angle
Adj. & Opp.	$\sqrt{\text{Adj.}^2+\text{Opp.}^2}$	———	———	$\text{Tan.} = \dfrac{\text{Opp.}}{\text{Adj.}}$	$\text{Cot.} = \dfrac{\text{Opp.}}{\text{Adj.}}$
Adj. & Angle	$\dfrac{\text{Adj.}}{\text{Cos.}}$	———	Adj. x Tan.	———	90°-Angle
Opp. & Angle	$\dfrac{\text{Opp.}}{\text{Sin.}}$	Opp. x Cot.	———	———	90°-Angle

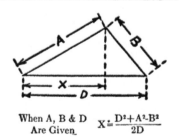

When A, B & D Are Given $\quad X = \dfrac{D^2+A^2\text{-}B^2}{2D}$

GLOSSARY

ACCELEROMETER. An instrument for indicating or recording speed.

ACETYLENE. A colorless gas with a disagreeable odor; it burns with a yellow, sooty flame by itself. Combined with oxygen, it makes a hot, clear welding flame.

AERIAL TRAIN. One or more gliders towed behind an airplane.

AEROBATICS. Intentional aerial acrobatics which are not necessary in normal air navigation.

AEROMETER. A device for weighing the tension of gases, such as air, to determine weight and density.

AEROSTAT. A type of aircraft whose support in the air is due to buoyancy derived from lighter-than-air gases.

AGING MAGNETS. A method of subjecting magnets to treatment similar to that which they will encounter in service. This causes the magnet to lose its maximum strength, but it will retain the remaining strength for a long period of time.

AILERON. A hinged or pivoted auxiliary airfoil, usually part of the trailing edge of a wing. Its primary purpose is to give the airplane a rolling movement. The main types of ailerons are:

(1) *Differential*—ailerons hinged so that the raising of one exceeds the drooping of the other, thus equalizing aileron drag.

(2) *Frise*—ailerons hinged some distance back of their leading edges so that when the ailerons are drooped their leading edges are screened by the wing; but when one of these ailerons is raised, its leading edge projects below the undersurface of the wing—thus creating a drag force to compensate the drag of the drooped aileron on the opposite wing. This prevents "yawning."

(3) *Interplane*—ailerons hinged between two wings, but not a part of either wing.

193

(4) *Skew*—ailerons with hinge lines that extend out toward the wing tips at angles of perhaps 10 or 15 degees; this places the bulk of the aileron area at the maximum distance from the longitudinal axis of the airplane, giving unusual lateral control at high angles of attack.

AIR BRAKES. Flaps which can be extended from the trailing edge of a wing, creating resistance and causing lower landing or diving speeds.

AIRFOIL. Any surface designed to secure a useful dynamic reaction when projected through the air.

AIRFOIL SECTION (or PROFILE). The cross section of an airfoil. A line perpendicular to the plane of this cross section is called "the axis of the airfoil."

AIR LINE. A straight line, the shortest distance between two points.

AIRFRAME. A British term for fuselage.

AIRPLANE. A heavier-than-air machine supported by the dynamic reactions of the air to fixed wings. Types of airplanes are listed in Chapter 3.

AIRPORT. A position on either water or land which is suitable for the landing or taking off of aircraft; it may include facilities for shelter, supply, and repair of aircraft—or it may be only a location for the discharge or loading of passengers or cargo.

AIR, PURE DRY. Approximately 78% nitrogen, 21% oxygen, 1% argon, and .03% carbon dioxide.

AIR SCOOP. An opening designed to "trap" air for ventilating purposes, as in oil coolers or carburetors.

AIRSCREW. A British term for propeller.

AIRSPEED INDICATOR. An instrument which indicates the speed of an airplane relative to the air; it is actuated by the pressure developed in a "pressure nozzle" outside of the airplane, and its readings are termed "indicated air speed." The instrument which measures the true airspeed of an airplane is called an "anemometer."

AIRWORTHINESS. A term which indicates conformity with requirements of the Civil Aeronautics Authority publications, approved by the Assistant Secretary of Commerce for Aeronautics.

ALCLAD. A sheet of duralumin "sandwiched" between thin sheets of pure aluminum.

ALCOA. The Aluminum Company of America; this abbreviation is frequently found on aluminum and aluminum alloy products.

ALIGNMENT. The adjustment of an object into a designed form or shape.

ALLOY. A metal treated or refined with one or more chemical elements so as to form a new material with different properties.

ALTIGRAPH. An altimeter combined with a recording mechanism.

ALTIMETER. An instrument for indicating the elevation of an aircraft above a given height. Most altimeters depend upon the deflection of a pressure-sensitive element for their indications. However, an equally efficient type is the "sound-ranging" altimeter, the indications of which depend on the measurement of the time required for a sound wave to travel from the airplane to the earth and back.

AMMETER. An electrical instrument which measures the flow of electrical current in a circuit. It is connected on the positive side of the circuit, between the generator and the power using unit.

AMPERE. A unit of electrical current flow; volts and amperes make watts, the unit of electrical power.

AMPHIBIAN. An airplane which can be operated from either land or water.

ANCHOR, SEA. An open fabric bag which fills with water and acts as an anchor for a seaplane; it may include a tripping or collapsing device, and is sometimes called a "drogue."

ANEMOMETER. An instrument for indicating or measuring the speed of an air stream.

ANGLE, ACUTE. An angle of less than 90 degrees.

ANGLE, AILERON or ELEVATOR. The angular displacement of an aileron or elevator control surface from its neutral position; it is positive when the trailing edge of the surface is below the neutral position.

ANGLE, OBTUSE. An angle greater than 90 degrees.

ANGLE, RUDDER. The acute angle between the rudder and plane

of symmetry of an airplane. It is positive when the trailing edge is moved to the left.

ANNEALING. A heat treatment designed to refine and relieve strain in a metal; its purpose generally is to soften the material for additional work.

ANODIZING. A process which forms an oxide coating on aluminum alloy materials.

ANTIDRAG WIRE. A wire designed to resist forces acting parallel to the chord of the wing of an airplane and in the direction of flight; it is generally enclosed in the wing.

APRON. A hard surface of considerable extent in front of a hangar or aircraft shelter.

ARGON. A gas of great density which comprises a small part of normal air.

ARMATURE. The rotating element in motors, magnetos, generators, etc.

ARRESTING GEAR. A hook in the tail section of a landplane which will facilitate landings on an aircraft carrier by catching a heavy cable stretched across the deck of the ship.

ARTIFICIAL HORIZON. An instrument which will indicate the position of an airplane relative to the earth when "flying blind" (in clouds or fog).

ASH. A springy, hard, and tough wood sometimes used in aircraft construction.

ATTITUDE. The position of an aircraft as determined by the inclination of its axes to the earth.

A.F.C. Automatic flight control, a mechanism similar to the automatic pilot, especially designed for bombing planes.

AUTOMATIC PILOT. A mechanism which, when properly adjusted, will keep an airplane on a straight level course without assistance from the pilot.

A.P.U. Auxiliary power unit, a small gasoline motor used to charge batteries and start other motors in large airplanes.

AXES OF AN AIRPLANE. Three fixed reference lines, usually intersecting at a single point, each perpendicular to the other two.

AXIS. A reference line, about which there is a rotating movement.

BABBITT METAL. An antifriction alloy of copper, tin, and zinc.

BALL BEARINGS and ROLLER BEARINGS. Metal balls or rollers which eliminate sliding friction by providing a rolling contact with cones and races. They cannot be tightened or adjusted, and should not be lubricated by pressure.

BANK AND TURN INDICATORS. Instruments which indicate the angular velocity of a turn or the inclination of a wing tip toward the earth in a "banking" maneuver. In level flight these instruments may further indicate the tendencies of an airplane to deviate from a straight course.

BAR SECTION. A structural section with more width than thickness; light bars are sometimes called "straps."

BAROMETER. An instrument used for measuring atmospheric pressure.

BAROGRAPH. An instrument for recording barometric or static pressure.

BAY. A term used in connection with body parts. For example, "bomb bay," a section between adjacent bulkheads or frame positions in a bombing plane.

BELL CRANK. A double lever or crank arm in which the cranks are at approximately right angles to one another, their purpose being to afford a means of changing the direction of motions—as in the case of control rods running from the fuselage and making a right angular connection to control rods running back to an aileron.

BELT, SAFETY. A belt or strap which secures a pilot or passenger to his seat.

BEND RADIUS. The radius of the curved portion of a part.

BEVEL. The condition of any construction forming an angle. A bevel is "closed" when it comprises an angle of less than 90 degrees; it is "opened" when the angle is greater than 90 degrees.

BIPLANE, ORTHOGONAL. A biplane which does not have staggered wings.

BIRCH. Sometimes used with spruce to form laminated wood parts for airplanes; it is also used to cover the leading edges of some airfoils.

BLADE BACK. The side of a propeller blade which corresponds to the upper surface of a wing.

BLADE FACE. The side of a propeller blade which corresponds to the lower surface of a wing; this is sometimes called the "thrust face" or "driving face."

BOOSTER MAGNETO. An auxiliary magneto used for the production of strong sparks for starting purposes.

BORE. Usually the size of a cylindrical hole in a part.

BORING MILL. A machine designed to bore holes by means of a rotating part (called the "bed"), to which the work is fastened.

BOURDON TUBE. A tube which will straighten itself out when pressure is applied internally; it is used frequently in pressure- and temperature-indicating instruments.

BRAZING. A process of sticking metal parts together with melted brass or hard solder.

B.T.U. British thermal unit, the heat required to raise the temperature of one pound of water one degree Fahrenheit.

BRONZE. A metal containing copper and tin, somewhat harder than Babbitt metal, but softer than case-hardened steel. It is often used for piston pin bearings.

BUCK. A big "move" jig, generally used in final assembly operations on large airplanes.

BULB-ANGLE. A right angle of metal having the outer edge of one flange enlarged in a circular manner, so as to provide additional stiffness to a part.

BULKHEADS. Lateral partitions of a fuselage or very large wing.

BUTTERFLY VALVE. A valve which appears to have a "wing" on each side of its axis, similar in design to the damper of a stove pipe.

CABANE. The framework which supports the wing of an airplane at the fuselage.

CABLE. 608 feet, or $\frac{1}{10}$ of a nautical mile.

CALIBRATE. To mark off the correct graduations on instruments or scales.

CALORIE. The heat necessary to raise the temperature of one gram of water one degree Centigrade. Such heat is measured on a "calorimeter."

CAM. An eccentric surface which imparts variable motion to the valve mechanism of engines.

CAM FOLLOWER. An engine part on the contour surface of a cam, to which motion is imparted by the cam.

CAMBER. The rise in the curve of an airfoil section from its chord. "Upper camber" usually means the upper surface of an airfoil, while "lower camber" means the lower surface.

CANTILEVER. A word generally used to designate monoplane wings which lack exterior supports; grammatically, it means "a projecting arm." Monoplane wings braced with struts are said to be of semi-cantilever design.

CARBURETOR. A mechanical device which mixes liquid fuel and air to form a combustible mixture for a gasoline engine.

CASE HARDENING. The process of hardening the outer surface, or crust, of a metal.

CATAPULT. A mechanical device for launching airplanes from ships which are not otherwise equipped as aircraft carriers.

CAVITATION, PROPELLER. The tendency of a propeller to form a rarified area ahead of and in the vicinity of propeller movements.

CEDAR. A wood sometimes used in aircraft work, especially in the form of plywood; its structure is uniform and can be easily worked.

CENTER SECTION. This term usually designates the center part of the wing. However, it may also include that part of the fuselage to which the wing is attached.

CENTRIFUGAL FORCE. The force which causes a body moving in a curved path to press outward, away from the center of the curve.

CENTRIPETAL FORCE. The force which causes a body to resist centrifugal force.

CHAMFER. To bevel a sharp edge.

CHANNEL SECTION. A structural section comprising a web for depth and flanges on a single side (top and bottom). Such sections are designed to carry vertical loads, and have little strength if the web is placed in a horizontal position. They may be solid sections or built up from a flat plate (web) and two angles (flanges).

CHINE. The intersection of the bottom with the sides or deck of a seaplane float or hull.

CHORD. The width of a wing, or other airfoil section, at any given point.

CIRCUIT BREAKER. A device in a primary circuit used to interrupt the circuit.

CLIMB INDICATOR. A pressure-operated instrument which shows the rate of ascent or descent of an airplane.

CLOTH. Bleached fabric, which has not been doped or specially treated for aeronautic use.

CLOCKWISE. A rotation in the direction indicated by the movement of clock hands.

COCKPIT. The open space in an airplane for the pilot or passengers. An enclosed cockpit is called a "cabin," or "compartment."

COMBUSTION. The process of burning.

COMPASS. An instrument to determine direction by means of a needle rotating about a compass card or direction control, its reference point being north.

COMPASS ROSE. A huge compass card, upon which an airplane can be placed in order to compensate and determine the accuracy of its compass.

CONCENTRIC. A word pertaining to circles with a common center.

CONDENSATION. The return of water vapor in the air to a solid or liquid state.

CONDENSER. A storage space for electricity.

CONDUCTION. The transference of heat or electricity from one part of a body to another.

CONNECTING ROD. A rod with a bearing at each end connecting a piston or wrist pin with an off-set (crank pin) on the crankshaft.

CONTROL COLUMN, or JOYSTICK. The control in the pilot's cockpit of an airplane which moves the elevators and ailerons.

CORROSION. The deterioration of exposed surfaces due to climatic conditions or immersion in water, acids, etc.

COULOMB. The unit of electrical quantity, or the amount of electricity that will flow in a circuit in one second with a pressure of one volt and a resistance of one ohm.

COUNTER-CLOCKWISE. A rotation opposite to the direction indicated by the movement of clock hands.

COWL FLAP. A movable partition which will control the heat of an airplane engine by opening or closing—thus governing the amount of air that circulates around the cylinder heads of the engine.

COWLING. A removable covering which extends over or around the engine, and sometimes over part of the fuselage or nacelle as well.

CRANKCASE. The cast basic section of an engine where crankshaft bearings and other parts are mounted, and to which the cylinders are fastened.

CRANKSHAFT. The main shaft on an engine, to which rotary motion is given by the piston through a connecting rod and an off-set throw on the shaft.

CROSS TIES. The more important structural members which extend laterally over the top and bottom of a fuselage.

CUBE ROOT OF A NUMBER. A figure which, when multiplied by itself twice, will equal the number. For example, $3 \times 3 \times 3 = 27$; hence, 3 is the cube root of 27.

CYLINDER. A hollow cylindrical section designed to permit reciprocating motion of a piston placed therein.

DECALAGE. The acute angle between the wing chords of a triplane or multiplane.

DEFORMATION. The alteration in the form of a substance caused by stress; it may be tensile, compressive, bending, or shearing—depending on the type of stress.

DE-ICER. A system whereby hot air is distributed from a motor through a rubber "de-icer boot" along the leading edges of a wing or tail section in order to break up ice formations which will alter the flying efficiency of an airplane.

DENSITY. The relative weight per unit volume of a substance as compared with the weight of the same volume of water.

DEVELOPED LENGTH (D.L.). The actual over-all length of any finished part.

DEVELOPED WIDTH (D.W.). The actual over-all width of any finished part.

DIAMAGNETIC SUBSTANCES. Materials which are feebly repelled by magnetism.

DIATHERMANOUS. A condition which enables a substance freely to transmit heat waves, or rays.

DIRECTIONAL RADIO. An aircraft radio which supplements a compass; radio bearings enable the pilot to determine his position.

DISTILLATES. Naphtha products, obtained by distilling crude oils.

DISTORTION. A synonym for "deformation."

DRAG. The forces which resist the forward motion of an airplane. These forces are called "parasite drag" if they are produced by any part of an airplane except a wing.

DRAG WIRE. Any wire or cable, either internal or external, designed to resist drag forces.

DRIFT INDICATOR. An instrument for determining the angle at which an airplane tends to depart from a straight path, due to lateral velocity.

DURALUMIN or DURAL. An aluminum alloy which is frequently used in the construction of airplanes; its chemical composition and physical properties are approximately as follows:

> Copper, 3.5 to 4.5 per cent
> Manganese, 0.4 to 1 per cent
> Magnesium, 0.2 to 0.75 per cent
> Aluminum, 92 per cent, minimum
> Tensile strength, 55,000 PSI
> Specific gravity, 2.85, maximum

ECCENTRIC. A term which, mechanically, designates circles not having the same center.

ELECTRICITY, STATIC. Electricity at rest or stationary, with no current flow. Friction between dissimilar metals is the commonest source of static electricity, which is a flying hazard because sparks of static electricity—even at some distance—can ignite a tank of gasoline.

ELECTRODE. An electrical conductor used at a terminal position in a circuit (as on a welding torch, arc lamp, etc.).

ELECTROLYTE. The mixture of concentrated sulphuric acid and distilled water in a storage battery.

ELECTROMAGNETISM. The magnetism produced around a conducting medium by an electrical current.

ELEVATOR. A movable auxiliary airfoil attached to the horizontal stabilizer in the tail section of an airplane; its purpose is to give the airplane a pitching movement.

EMPENNAGE. The tail-surface group (rudder, elevators, and stabilizers).

EMPIRICAL FORMULA. Any formula based upon experience which cannot be scientifically proved.

ENGINE. The power plant of an airplane, classified according to its shape and operation. (See examples in the illustrations on page 204.)

ENGINE, DIESEL. An internal combustion engine depending solely on the heat of compression; fuel oil is injected under high pressure, and no ignition system or carburetor is required.

ENGINES, GEARED. Engines with gears, as in an automobile; these gears allow for different speeds of rotation for the engine and its propeller.

ETCHING, PROPELLER. A process of treating the surface of metal propellers so as to show up flaws and cracks.

FAHRENHEIT SCALE. The temperature scale which indicates the freezing of water at 32° above zero, and the boiling of water at 212° above zero.

FAIRING. An auxiliary covering, usually without appreciable strength, which is streamlined so as to reduce the resistance or drag of the part to which it is fitted.

FARAD. The unit of capacity of a condenser when it will hold one coulomb of electricity when a pressure of one volt is applied across it.

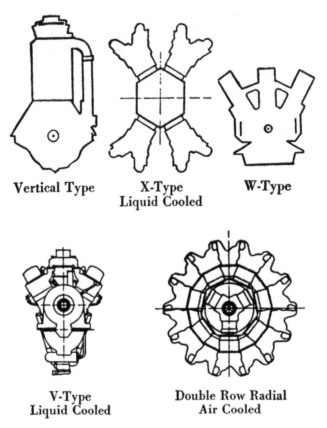

Vertical Type   X-Type   W-Type
                    Liquid Cooled

V-Type   Double Row Radial
Liquid Cooled   Air Cooled

CLASSIFICATIONS OF AIRCRAFT ENGINES

FERRULE. Metal fittings or wire wrappings whose purpose is to prevent the splitting of wooden parts or the loosening of wire terminals, etc.

FILLETING. The process of rounding out rough joints into smooth curves, so as to increase the streamline possibilities of an airplane.

FIN. A fixed surface, sometimes adjustable, parallel to the longitudinal axis of an airplane; its purpose is to enhance stability.

FIREWALL. A solid bulkhead, usually made of steel, designed to isolate the engine from the remainder of the airplane so as to restrict fire to the engine compartment.

FITTING. Uniting parts to form a complete assembly. Types of fits are:

(1) *Drive fit*—for parts of such close dimensions they have to be driven together with blows.

(2) *Press fit*—for parts that must be pressed together, either mechanically or manually.

(3) *Running fit*—for parts that should be moved freely after being united.

(4) *Shrink fit*—for parts so closely dimensioned that one part must be expanded by heat before the other part can be placed within it; shrinkage occurs when the heated part cools, producing an exceedingly tight fit.

The word "fitting" may also designate a single small metal part.

FLANGE. A width of metal extending away at an angle from another width in a single section.

FLAP. A hinged or pivoted airfoil forming the rear part of a larger airfoil; its purpose is to vary the effective camber of the main airfoil. A flap is "split" when it is divided into two parts, each part with a different purpose. A flap designed to lower the speed of an airplane for diving or landing is called an "air brake."

FLETTNER FLAP. The trade name for a popular wing flap.

FLOAT. The watertight structure which gives buoyancy and stability to a seaplane on the surface of water. Also, there is a float in the carburetor of an airplane engine; its purpose is to regulate the flow of fuel into the carburetor.

FLUTTER. The vibration of an airplane part in flight.

FLUX. A material used in welding to prevent the formation of oxides, nitrides, etc.

FOOT POUND. The expenditure of energy required to raise a weight of one pound through a distance of one foot against the action of gravity.

FORCE, COERCIVE. The force needed to demagnetize a magnet.

FUSE. A soft metal unit in an electrical circuit, designed to melt and break the circuit when the current reaches a danger point.

FUSELAGE. A streamlined structure which houses the passengers, cargo, and crew of an airplane.

GALVANOMETER. A sensitive instrument which measures the voltage of an electrical current.

GEAR, FLOTATION. The emergency gear which enables a landplane to float when forced to alight on water.

GEAR, GROUND. *See* Landing Gear.

GENERATOR. A machine which transforms mechanical power into electrical power.

GLUE, CASEIN. A glue made from casein which is precipitated from sour milk curds with hydrochloric acid; this glue is highly resistant to water.

GRAIN. $\frac{1}{7000}$ of a pound avoirdupois, or .0648 of a gram.

GRAM, CALORIE (gm. cal.). The heat required to raise one gram of water from 14.5° C. to 15.5° C.

GRAVITY, SPECIFIC. The "density" of a substance.

GRINDER. A machine used to give a high finish and accurate dimensions to a part being manufactured.

GROUNDSPEED METER. An instrument which measures the speed of an airplane relative to the ground.

GUSSET. A small triangular brace used to strengthen corners in a structure, especially at wing rib joints.

GYROSCOPE, or GYRO. A rotating wheel or disc which will rotate about any axis upon which it is turned.

HARD PINE. A tough, uniform wood which can be used for the framework in a light airplane.

HICKORY. A tough, springy, hard-surfaced wood which is sometimes used for tail skids and control levers.

HOOD, N.A.C.A. The ring portion of N.A.C.A. cowling.

HORN. A short lever attached to an airplane control surface. For example, elevator horn, rudder horn, etc.

HORSEPOWER (ONE). The energy necessary to raise 550 pounds one foot in one second against the force of gravity.

HULL, SEAPLANE. That portion of a flying boat which furnishes buoyancy on the surface of water.

HYDROMETER. A graduated glass syringe used to determine the specific gravity of storage-battery solutions.

HYGROMETER. An instrument which indicates humidity as a result of the expansion and contraction of human hairs. These indications may be recorded on a "hygrograph."

INBOARD (I.B.). Toward the fuselage from the wing tips of an airplane.

I-BEAM SECTION. The cross section of a structural part, made in the form of a capital I.

IGNITION. The process of setting fire to fuel or fuel vapor in an internal-combustion engine.

INCLINOMETER. An instrument for indicating the attitude of an airplane.

INDICATOR, FLIGHT. An instrument which includes a fore-and-aft inclinometer, a lateral inclinometer, and a turn indicator.

INDRAFT, or INFLOW. The flow of air from in front of a propeller into the blades.

INTERCOSTAL. An inside brace or frame member which supports a covering along its inside area.

INTERRUPTER. The circuit breaker or breaker points in the primary circuit of a magneto.

INTERSECTION. The point at which two or more lines cross.

JIG. A pattern, framework, or form so dimensioned and aligned as to facilitate the construction of identical parts.

JOINER, WOOD. A machine used to finish the narrow edges of a wooden board.

JOULE. The amount of energy necessary to cause the flow of one coulomb of electricity under a pressure of one volt.

KEEL SURFACE. The surface seen in the side view of an airplane.

KILOGRAM. 1000 grams, or 2.204 pounds.

KILOGRAM-CALORIE (kg.-cal.). .01 of the heat necessary to raise the temperature of one kilogram of water from 0° C. to 100° C.

KILOMETER. 1000 meters.

KILOWATT. 1000 watts, or 1.34 h.p.

KINETIC ENERGY. The capacity of a moving body to perform work.

KNOT. A nautical mile, 6,080 feet, sometimes used to measure the speed or velocity of an airplane.

LANDING GEAR. The wheels and understructure which support an airplane on the surface of the earth. Landing gear is retractable if it can be withdrawn into the body or wings of an airplane to secure better flying efficiency.

LATERAL. A word meaning crosswise. For example, the lateral dimension of a wing is its span.

LATHE. A machine which rotates work so that material may be removed from a circumference with a cutting tool.

LEADING EDGE. The foremost edge of an airfoil, sometimes called "entering edge."

L.H. A blueprint abbreviation meaning "left hand." The left-hand side of an airplane is on the left side of an observer inside the ship and facing its nose. This is often called the "port side."

LEVER. A bar which will transfer a force from one point to another.

LIFT. The force which enables an airplane to fly.

LIGHTENING HOLE. Any hole cut in a part to decrease the weight of an airplane. The edges of the hole are usually flanged in order to prevent a loss of strength.

LODESTONE. A stone containing oxide of iron called magnetite, which acts like a magnetic needle in seeking the North Pole and which will attract other pieces of metal.

LONGERON. A fore-and-aft frame member in an airplane fuselage or nacelle.

LONGITUDINAL. Any lengthwise strength member which connects various transverse frames; or a reference line through the center of the fuselage of a conventional airplane.

LOOM. The web sections of wing ribs.

LUBRICATION. The use of oil or grease to protect metal parts or to eliminate friction between metal parts.

MACHINING. The finishing of objects and parts by means of a

machine such as a lathe, planer, boring mill, drill shaper, grinder, etc.

MAGNET. A piece of material which attracts other magnetic materials.

MAGNETISM, LAW OF. Like poles repel each other; unlike poles attract each other.

MAGNETO. An electrical device for the production and distribution of electricity.

MAHOGANY. *See* Walnut.

MANEUVERABILITY. That quality in an aircraft which makes it possible for a pilot to change its attitude.

MANUAL. Any operation accomplished by hand, rather than by a machine.

MAPLE. A strong, reliable wood sometimes used for small parts in airplanes.

MASS. The measure of the quantity of material in a body.

MEAN. A word meaning "average."

METAL, BASE. Metal to be welded; or the predominant metal in an alloy.

METAL, FERROUS. Any metal with an iron base.

METAL, FILLER. The material, usually in rod form, which is melted and deposited in making a weld.

MICARTA. The trade name for a laminated product sometimes used in aircraft work.

MOTOR, ELECTRIC. A machine which transforms electric power into mechanical power.

MOTOR MOUNT. The framework upon which an airplane engine is mounted.

NACELLE. An enclosed shelter, usually for a power plant.

NEOPRENE. An artificial rubber product.

NICKEL. An alloy used to toughen and strengthen steel.

NORMAL. Mechanically, means perpendicular.

NOSE. The bow, or foremost part, of an airplane.

NYLON. The trade name of a plastic material sometimes used as lining in airplane fuel cells.

OAK. A tough wood sometimes preferred in the construction of seaplane floats.

OUTBOARD (O.B.). Toward the wing tip from the fuselage of an airplane.

OHM. A unit of electrical resistance.

OIL PUMP. A mechanism used to circulate oil under pressure through parts of an airplane engine.

OLEO STRUT. A strut which depends on the flow of oil through an orifice for shock absorbing effect; this type of strut is widely used in retractable landing gear mechanisms.

OSCILLATION. A swinging to and fro, or a vibration.

OXYGEN. A colorless and odorless gas which supports combustion to a high degree; it comprises about 21 per cent of the air we breathe.

OXYGEN SYSTEM. The equipment used to supply pure oxygen to the passengers and crew of an airplane flying at an altitude of more than 20,000 feet. It comprises oxygen bottles with regulating valves connected by tubing to face masks.

PALNUT. A very thin steel nut with a shallow cup-shaped bottom face. Because it is self-locking, it is frequently used in making engine installations. Its AN number is 356.

PANEL. The single unit of construction in a wing which consists of several such units.

PARALLEL RULES. Two rules or straight edges attached to one another by pivoted bars so that their edges remain parallel no matter how far apart they may be.

PARAMAGNETIC SUBSTANCES. A material which is feebly magnetic.

PISTON. The sliding part of a cylinder, to which motion is usually imparted by expanding gases.

PISTON RING. A concentric ring inserted in a groove cut in the wall of a piston to maintain compression and to prevent the passage of too much oil to the combustion chamber.

PITCH OF A PROPELLER. The angle at which the propeller blades are turned. "Low pitch" generally provides the most power for a take-off. "High-pitch" is best for normal operating conditions after the take-off. When the blades of a propeller are stopped and turned so that they present the least aerodynamic resistance, they are "feathered." In seaplanes it is sometimes possible to "reverse" the pitch of a propeller; this produces a braking action which may either stop or maneuver the airplane into a desired position.

PITOT TUBE. A tube with an open end, attached to the exterior surface of an airplane so that the air meets the instrument head-on. Its purpose is to measure the impact pressure of the air, thus giving the pilot a reading on his airspeed indicator.

PLANER. A machine designed to plane or surface wood or metal parts.

PLAN FORM, or PLANIFORM. The projected drawing of a wing surface which shows the tapered or rectangular shape of the wing.

PLAN-VIEW DRAWING. An orthographic projection which shows the true shape of an object as viewed from the top.

PLYWOOD. Layers of veneer (wood) cemented by plastics under pressure; the grain of the wood sheets are usually at right angles to one another.

PRIMARY STRUCTURE (STRESS ANALYSIS). The main framework, including fittings and attachments, or any structural member upon which the safety of the airplane is dependent.

PRIMER. A pumping device to squirt raw gasoline into intake passages or cylinders to facilitate the starting of an engine.

PROFILE DRAWING. An orthographic projection which shows the shape of an object as viewed from the side. This is sometimes called a "side elevation" or "side view."

PROFILE THICKNESS. The maximum distance between the upper and lower contours of an airfoil.

PROPELLER. A series of surfaces so shaped that its rotation about an axis produces thrust. A "fixed-pitch" propeller produces uniform thrust at all times. "Variable" or "controllable" pitch propellers may be adjusted in flight for greatest operating efficiency. "Adjustable-pitch" propellers may be adjusted while stationary for any desired pitch.

PROPELLER, PUSHER. A propeller mounted behind, rather than in front of, the engine.

PROPELLER, TRACTOR. A propeller mounted in front of an engine.

PROPELLER BOSS. The reinforcement at the shank of the blade of a propeller, into which the hub is fitted or which fits into the hub.

PROPELLER HUB. A metal fitting mounted or formed on the propeller boss for the purpose of attaching the propeller to the engine shaft.

PROPELLER ROOT. Part of a propeller blade near the boss.

PULSATE. To throb or beat. This is a danger signal in airplane engines, because an engine should not pulsate as long as it is getting sufficient gas.

PYROMETER. A device for measuring the differences in temperatures of two adjoining pieces of metal (up to about 1500° F.) by means of a thermo-electric couple and a galvanometer. This device is said to be "mechanical" rather than electrical, if its purpose is to determine temperatures by measuring the expansion coefficients of dissimilar metals.

QUADRANT. A base, shaped like an arc, for control levers.

QUENCHING. The cooling of heated metal in a liquid for the purpose of tempering.

RECORDER, FLIGHT. An instrument for recording various reactions of an airplane in flight.

REFERENCE LINE. An imaginary line located at a given point in an airplane or part thereof. The centerline, shown so often in blueprints, is a reference line.

RETENTIVITY. The power of iron and steel to resist demagnetization.

R.H. A blueprint abbreviation meaning "right hand." The right side of an airplane is the right side of an observer inside the ship and facing its nose.

RIB. A fore and aft member of the wing structure of an airplane; it gives form to the wing section and transmits the load from the fabric or skin to the spars.

RIB, BOX. A solid rib, shaped like a box, at the junction of a wing and fuselage.

RIB, COMPRESSION. The stress-bearing ribs in the framework of a wing.

RIB, FALSE. A short form rib in the leading edge of a wing; its presence improves and maintains the camber of an airfoil.

RIB, FORM. A light, form-giving part used in airfoil construction.

RIGGER. One who helps assemble and align an airplane.

RIGGING. The assembly, adjustment, and alignment of airplane parts.

RIGGING POSITION. The position of an airplane when its longitudinal axis is parallel to the ground.

ROCKER ARM. The connecting link between the push rod and the valve stem in an airplane engine; its function is to actuate a valve.

RUDDER. A movable auxiliary airfoil which provides directional control (right or left movements) for an airplane.

RUDDER BAR. The foot bar which enables a pilot to move the rudder of an airplane.

RUDDER PEDAL. A pedal sometimes used in place of a bar to control a rudder.

RUNNERS, or SKIS. Staves used for landing airplanes on snow or ice; they replace landing-gear wheels when applicable.

SAND BLASTING. A method of cleaning metal surfaces with a high velocity jet of sand and air; it will roughen smooth surfaces for painting or plating, and removes oxides or corrosion.

SCALE EFFECT. The calculated differences in performance of a wind-tunnel model and a full-sized airplane in flight.

SELF-SEALING FUEL CELLS. Rubber cells designed to hold gasoline and usually contained in the wing of an airplane. These cells are popular in military craft because they are capable of sealing up leaks caused by bullet punctures.

SERVO UNIT. The actuating mechanism in an automatic pilot.

SHAPER. A machine which will finish metal surfaces to a desired shape by means of a tool which travels back and forth over the work.

SHEAR. A force which attacks an object in opposite directions from the side. Generally a thick cross section is required to enable a part to resist shear forces.

SHEAR BEAM. An auxiliary part designed to take local shear loads, transmitting them to parts of the structure where they can be absorbed or withstood.

SHIELDING. A method of blanketing the electrical system of an airplane engine to prevent interference with radio equipment.

SHIP. Slang for "airplane."

SHOCK ABSORBER. A device to reduce and absorb the shock to which landing gear is subjected; it is usually interposed between the main structure and the wheels, floats, skis, or tail skid.

SHRINKAGE. A reduction in the size of a body.

SHUTTERS. The same as "cowl flaps." (*See definition.*)

SIDE-ELEVATION DRAWING. A drawing which shows the true shape of an object as seen from one side.

SINE OF AN ANGLE. The vertical leg of a right triangle divided by the hypotenuse.

SKID. A runner used as part of the landing gear; it is usually attached to the tail cone, but in some instances skids have been attached to wing tips.

SKID FIN. A vertical surface placed fore and aft above a wing, designed to increase lateral stability.

SKIN. A covering—usually of metal, fabric, or wood—for the framework of an airplane.

SKIN FRICTION. Friction resulting from the application of a fluid (or air) force at a particular point on the skin of an airplane.

SLAT. A movable auxiliary airfoil incorporated in the leading edge of a wing. When opened, it forms a slot in the leading edge.

SLIPSTREAM. The stream of air produced by a propeller.

SLOT. The same as "slat." (*See definition.*)

SPAN. The longest dimension of an object, usually an airfoil.

SPECIFIC HEAT. The heat required to raise the temperature of one pound of any substance 1° F., expressed in terms of B.T.U.

SPHERE. A solid body with all points on its surface equidistant from its center.

SPIRIT LEVEL. A glass tube filled with spirits so that there is room for a single air bubble; the position of this bubble indicates the attitude of an airplane.

SPIRITS. A nonfreezing liquid used for filling compass bowls.

SPLICE. The joining of two pieces of rope, wire, or wood so that the joint is as strong as the material spliced.

SPOILER. A small plate which projects above the upper surface of a wing, disturbing the smooth flow of air and causing a loss of lift along with an increase in drag. Rarely used, except in experimental aircraft, it is sometimes called an *interceptor* and may supplement or replace a *wing flap*.

SPONSON. A protuberance from a flying boat hull, designed to increase the beam or provide lateral stability on the surface of water.

SPRAY STRIP. A strip along the hull of a flying boat, designed to alter the course of spray during a take-off or landing.

SPRUCE. A clean, silver-grained, smooth, strong, and light wood which is considered excellent material for light airplanes.

SQUARE ROOT OF A NUMBER. A figure which, when multiplied by itself, equals the number. For example, the square root of 4 is 2— because 2 × 2 equals 4.

STABILITY. The ability of a body to maintain its equilibrium.

STABILIZER. A fixed airfoil whose function is to provide stability in an airplane. Most stabilizers are either vertical or horizontal, and are included in the tail section of an airplane. They are sometimes called "tail planes" or "fins."

STAGGER. A design characteristic of airplanes having more than one wing; the wings are placed so that the top wing or wings are slightly ahead of the lower wing or wings, no one wing being directly over the other.

STATIC TUBE. A cylindrical tube with a number of small openings, fixed so that it will face the slipstream on the exterior of an airplane; its purpose is to measure static pressure.

STATOSCOPE. An instrument for detecting minute changes of altitude in an aircraft; its indications depend on changes in pressure as registered by the static tube.

STAY. A wire or tension member designed to strengthen or align wings or other parts of an airplane.

STEP. A break in the form of the bottom of a hull or float in a seaplane; its purpose is to reduce water resistance, eliminating suction and decreasing the area of wetted surfaces when the seaplane is gathering speed for a take-off.

STING. A light rod attached to and extending rearward from a body for convenience in mounting the body for a wind-tunnel test.

STORAGE BATTERY, AIRCRAFT. A leak-proof storage battery which will not discharge its liquids during violent maneuvers.

STREAMLINE FORM. A solid body, shaped so as to present the least resistance to a fluid (either water or air).

STRESSES, FIVE TYPES OF. (1) Compression, caused by squeezing an object. (2) Tension, caused by stretching. (3) Shearing, caused by forces which tend to cut an object in two. (4) Bending. (5) Torsion, caused by twisting.

STRINGER. A longitudinal strip of material, to which the skin of an airplane may be attached; its strength is comparatively slight, since its purpose is merely to distribute the forces brought to bear on various parts of the skin.

STRUT. The compression member in a bound or girded frame. "Interplane struts" are situated between the wings of a multiplane. A "drag strut" is a fore-and-aft compression member of the internal bracing system of a wing.

SUBLIMATION. The conversion of solids to vapor by heat without a process of liquefaction.

SUMP. A cavity which collects used engine oil and from which the oil is pumped back to the tank.

SUPERCHARGER. A mechanical device which makes it possible for an airplane to fly at great altitudes by providing the engine with a greater supply of oxygen than could normally be induced at various atmospheric pressures and temperatures. The four supercharger types are:

(1) *Centrifugal*—a type employing rotating impellers to generate centrifugal force, which can be used for the compression and transmission of air against resistance.

(2) *Positive-driven*—a type driven at a fixed speed ratio from the engine shaft by gears, etc.

(3) *Rotary-blower*—a type which includes one or more slow speed rotors, revolving in a stationary case.

(4) *Turbo*—a type driven by a turbine, operated by exhaust gases from the engine.

SURFACE, CONTROL. An auxiliary airfoil which can be moved by the pilot so as to change the attitude of an airplane; ailerons, elevators, and rudders are the most common control surfaces.

SYMBOLS. Letters (as from the Greek alphabet) used to denote various factors, vital to aircraft production and operation. For example, "T" is the symbol for thrust.

SYMMETRICAL (SYM.). An object, such as a fuselage, with two sides identical.

SYMMETRY, PLANE OF. A vertical reference line through the longitudinal axis of a part that is symmetrical.

TAB, TRIMMING. An auxiliary airfoil attached to a control surface; its purpose is to reduce the control force required for level flight.

TACHOMETER. An instrument which registers the revolutions per minute (RPM) of an airplane engine.

TAIL WHEEL. A small wheel used in place of a skid on the tail cone of an airplane.

TANK, FIXED. A tank which cannot be dropped from an airplane in flight. This is the antithesis of a "slip tank."

TANK, SERVICE. A fixed fuel tank near an engine; it draws fuel from other tanks in order to supply the engine.

TANK, SLIP. A fuel tank which may be dropped from an airplane in an emergency.

TEMPERING. A term generally applied to the heat treatment of metals for hardness.

TEMPLATE. A pattern, from which sections of an airplane (including rivet holes, drilled holes, coverings, etc.) are determined and marked out.

THERMOCOUPLE. A "thermoelectric" couple device, consisting of two dissimilar metals which, when connected at the ends only, so as to form a complete circuit, will produce an electric current only when one end is more highly heated than the other.

THERMOGRAPH. An instrument for recording temperature.

THERMOMETER. An instrument which determines temperature.

THIMBLE. A small metal ring over which a wire can be looped without chafing or sharp bends.

THIOKOL. An artificial rubber product frequently used in self-sealing fuel cells and fuel lines.

THROTTLE. The control lever which enables the pilot of an airplane to operate the butterfly valve of a carburetor.

THRUST BEARING. A bearing which transmits propeller thrust, acting through the crankshaft to the crankcase of an airplane engine.

THRUST LINE. A reference line. (*See definition.*)

TIPPING. A word which indicates the protective sheet-metal covering sometimes used on the tips of propeller blades.

TIP RADIUS. The distance from the tip of a propeller blade to the propeller hub. This is also called "propeller radius."

TOGGLE. A short crossbar of wood or metal, fitted at the end of a rope; the rope passes through the center of the bar in a shouldered groove. By slipping it through the eye in the end of another rope, two lengths of rope can be readily connected or disconnected.

TOLERANCE. The variation from absolute accuracy that is allowed in making measurements.

TORQUE. The moment of force which causes an object or machine to rotate.

TORSIONAL STRESS. Stress produced by twisting.

TRANSFORMER. A device consisting of one or more induction coils which may be used either for raising or for lowering electric pressure.

TRANSITION. Commonly known as a "square to round," this is a part with a square base which gradually changes to a round contour at its top.

TRANSVERSE FRAME. A cross-frame member in a fuselage, usually ring shaped.

TRIMMING FLAP. Same as "tab, trimming." (*See definition.*)

T-SECTIONS. Structural sections shaped like a capital T, the vertical leg usually acting as a web while the horizontal part is a double flange.

TUNGSTEN. An alloy which gives extreme hardness and heat-resisting properties to steel.

TURNBUCKLE. A device for tightening wire or cable, fully explained in the chapter on Shop Practice.

UNDERCARRIAGE. Same as "landing gear." (*See definition.*)

VALVE. A part designed to control the flow of intake and exhaust gases to and from the cylinders of an airplane engine.

VANADIUM. An alloy which strengthens steel.

VARIABLE. Any factor which may have a change in values.

VEGETABLE OIL. Castor oil, used in some types of airplane engines.

VENEER. Thin sheets of wood.

VENTURI. A short tube with flaring ends and a narrow hole in between; its chief function is to measure the velocity of air currents. Sometimes it furnishes the power for gyroscopic instruments, but generally it is used to increase the flow of air in a carburetor. It may be further combined with a pitot tube to obtain indicated airspeed readings.

VIBRATION. An oscillation, quivering, or movement back and forth.

VISCOSIMETER. A device which determines the viscosity of oils by measuring the time required for a given quantity of oil at a given temperature to flow through a hole of a given size.

VOLT. A unit of electrical pressure.

VOLTMETER. An instrument for indicating the number of volts in an electrical circuit.

WALNUT. Wood of excellent quality, used extensively in the manufacture of fixed-pitch propellers for light airplanes. This same description applies to mahogany.

WARP. Changing the form of a wing by twisting.

WASH. Disturbance in the air, caused by the movements of an airfoil.

WASHIN. The permanent warping of a wing; this causes an increase in the angle of attack near the wing tip.

WASHOUT. The permanent warping of a wing so that the angle of attack is decreased near the wing tip.

WASTE GATE. A supercharging control.

WATER PUMP. A pump used to circulate cooling fluids in a water-cooled engine.

WATT. A unit of electrical power; it is the power due to a current of one ampere under a pressure of one volt.

WATTMETER. An instrument for measuring the power expended in an electrical circuit.

WEB. The depth unit of an I-beam section; it furnishes strength for the vertical loads for which beams (spars, etc.) are designed.

WELDING. The uniting of metals in a plastic or molten state, with or without mechanical pressure. Following are some of the principal welding classifications:

(1) *Automatic*—welding with automatic equipment.

(2) *Butt Joint*—welding two pieces of metal which are "butted" together, side to side or end to end.

(3) *Fillet*—welding at the intersections of two surfaces of lap, corner, or tee joints.

(4) *Flush*—welding so that no excess metal is visible at the point where the weld is made.

(5) *Fusion*—welding without the application of mechanical pressure or blows.

(6) *Gas*—a fusion-welding process in which welding heat is obtained from burning gases.

(7) *Manual*—welding without mechanical equipment.

(8) *Plug*—welding two parts by filling in the hole of one part.

(9) *Metal Arc*—a fusion-welding process in which welding heat is obtained by means of an electric arc between the base metal and an electrode. The base metal acts as a conductor to complete the electrical circuit.

(10) *Tack*—welding parts temporarily by depositing "spots" of filler-

rod metal at various points along a joint. This usually precedes a regular welding process, especially when working with large parts.

(11) *Tee Joint*—welding two parts in the form of a T.

For further data on welding, see the chapter on Assembly.

WINDMILL. An air-driven screw which may power auxiliary equipment on an airplane.

WINDOW, INSPECTION. A small, transparent window in the wing of an airplane to allow inspection of the interior.

WIND TUNNEL. A long chamber, through which a steady stream of air may be drawn or forced in order to test airplane models and airfoils. Some wind tunnels are large enough to test full-sized airplanes. Measuring devices in the tunnel record instantly all reactions of the airplane, airfoil, or model to the air stream.

WING. A general term which designates one or more airfoil supporting surfaces in an airplane.

WING RIB. A fore-and-aft member of the wing structure of an airplane; it gives the wing form and transmits pressure from the skin to the spars.

WING ROOT. The center section of a wing, or where it is attached to the fuselage of an airplane.

WING SPAR. The principal transverse member in the wing structure of an airplane.

WING-TIP RAKE. A term which refers to the shape of the wing tip when the tip edge is relatively straight but not parallel to the plane of symmetry.

WING TRUSS. The framework which transmits wing loads to the fuselage of an airplane; it comprises struts, wires, tie rods, spars, etc.

WIRE DRAWING. The process of drawing sections of metal through eyelets of given sizes to form wire. The drawing may be done with either hot or cold metals; friction creates enough heat to allow a smooth surface in cold wire drawing. Small sizes of wire must be drawn several times, since the diameter reduction in a single drawing is limited.

WIRE, LANDING. A wire designed to resist forces in the opposite direction to the normal direction of lift; it is sometimes called "anti-lift wire" since one of its functions is to oppose lift wire and prevent distortion of the structure when such wires are overtightened.

WIRE, LIFT. A wire or cable which transmits lift from the outer portion of the wing to the fuselage or nacelle of an airplane; this is sometimes called "flying wire."

WIRE, SAFETY. A wire which prevents the turning of a nut, bolt, or turnbuckle barrel.

WIRE, STAGGER. A wire which connects the upper and lower surfaces of an airplane; it is often called "incidence wire" and usually lies in a plane parallel to the plane of symmetry.

WOOD, LAMINATED. A product formed by gluing or otherwise uniting sheets or "laminations" of wood. Laminated wood differs from plywood in that the grain of alternate plies in the latter are crossed at right angles, while the grain of all plies in the former are substantially parallel.

WORKING STRESS. The maximum unit stress, to which parts of a structure should be subjected.

YAWING. The movements of the nose of an airplane to the right or left (or about the vertical axis).

YAWMETER. An instrument for measuring the angle of yaw.

ZERO, ABSOLUTE. 273° below Centigrade zero, or 459.4° below Fahrenheit zero.

ZERO LIFT LINE. A line through the trailing edge of a wing; it is parallel to the direction of the wind when the lift is zero.

BIBLIOGRAPHY

Aeronautical Books

ABC of Aviation, by V. W. Page; Norman W. Henley Publishing Co.
Aeronautical Engineering, by H. Nelson; George Newnes, Ltd.
Aeronautics Simplified, by E. G. Vetter; Foster Stewart Publishing Corp.
Aerosphere, 1942; Aircraft Publications.
Air Annual of the British Empire; Pitman Publishing Corp.
Aircraft Apprentice, The, by Leslie MacGregor; Pitman Publishing Corp.
Aircraft Assembly, by C. F. Marschner; Pitman Publishing Corp.
Aircraft Blueprint Reading, by Almen and Mead; Pitman Publishing Corp.
Aircraft Blueprints and How to Read Them, by Carl Norcross; McGraw-Hill Book Co.
Aircraft Construction, by D. Hay Surgeoner; Longmans, Green & Co.
Aircraft Detail Drafting, by Norman Meadowcraft; McGraw-Hill Book Co.
Aircraft Electricity, by N. J. Clark and H. E. Corbitt; Ronald Press.
Aircraft Engine Design, by Joseph Liston; McGraw-Hill Book Co.
Aircraft Engine Maintenance, by D. J. Brimm and H. E. Boggess; Pitman Publishing Corp.
Aircraft Engine Mechanic's Manual, by C. J. Moors; Ronald Press.
Aircraft Engine and Metal Finishes, by M. A. Coler; Pitman Publishing Corp.
Aircraft Inspection, by E. E. Wissman; McGraw-Hill Book Co.
Aircraft Inspection Methods, by N. C. Bartholomew; Pitman Publishing Corp.

224 *Bibliography*

Aircraft Lofting and Template Layout, With Descriptive Geometry, by Howard Thrasher; Aviation Press.

Aircraft Materials and Processes, by G. F. Titterton; Pitman Publishing Corp.

Aircraft Mathematics, by S. A. Walling; Macmillan Co.

Aircraft Mechanic's Pocket Manual, by J. A. Ashkouti; Pitman Publishing Corp.

Aircraft Power Plant Manual, by G. B. Manly; Frederick J. Drake & Co.

Aircraft Propellers, by C. M. Harlocher; Aero Publishers.

Aircraft Radio and Electrical Equipment, by H. K. Morgan; Pitman Publishing Corp.

Aircraft Riveting, by Albert H. Nisita; McGraw-Hill Book Co.

Aircraft Sheet Metal Workers' Manual, by Robert C. Look; Goodheart-Willcox Co.

Aircraft Welding, by L. S. Elzea; McGraw-Hill Book Co.

Aircraft Year Book, by the Aeronautical Chamber of Commerce of America, Inc.; D. Van Nostrand Co.

Air Navigation, by Phillip Weems; McGraw-Hill Book Co.

Air Navigation and Meteorology, by Richard Duncan; Goodheart-Willcox Co.

Air Piloting, by Virgil Simmons; Ronald Press.

Airplane Design, by E. P. Warner; McGraw-Hill Book Co.

Airplane Design Manual, by F. K. Teichman; Pitman Publishing Corp.

Airplane and Its Components, The, by W. R. Sears; John Wiley & Sons.

Airplane and Its Engine, The, by Chatfield, Taylor, and Ober; McGraw-Hill Book Co.

Airplane Maintenance, by Younger, Bonnalie, and Ward; McGraw-Hill Book Co.

Airplane Servicing Manual, by V. W. Page; Norman W. Henley Publishing Co.

Airplane Sheet Metal Construction, by William Baudette; Institute Press.

Airplane Structural Analysis and Design, by Ernest E. Sechler; John Wiley & Sons.

Airplanes and Elementary Engineering, by D. J. Brimm; International Textbook Co.

Aviation Dictionary and Reference Guide, by H. E. Baughman; Aero Publishers.

Aviation Engineer; International Textbook Co.

Aviation from the Ground Up, by G. B. Manly; Frederick J. Drake & Co.

Aviation Handbook, by Warner and Johnston; McGraw-Hill Book Co.

Autogiro and How To Fly It, by Reginald Brie; Pitman Publishing Corp.

Blue Book of American Aviation; Aviation Statistics Institute of America.

Civil Aeronautics Authority Publications (Published by U. S. Government Printing Office, Washington, D. C.), as follows:

> *Accidents and Casualties*
> *State Air Legislation*
> *Flight Instructors' Manual*
> *Airport Lighting*
> *Air Marking*
> *Primary Ground Instruction*
> *Civil Air Regulations*
> *Civil Air Journal Bulletins*
> *Nomenclature for Aeronautics*
> *Technical Reports*

Complete Model Aircraft Manual, by E. T. Hamilton; Dodd, Mead & Co.

Elements of Practical Aerodynamics, by Bradley Jones; John Wiley & Sons, Inc., 1942.

Getting a Job in Aviation, by Carl Norcross; McGraw-Hill Book Co.

Getting Them into the Blue, by E. K. Gann; Thomas Y. Crowell Co.

History of Aviation, by Wead and Allen; International Textbook Co.

How to Do Aircraft Sheet Metal Work, by Carl Norcross and J. P. Quinn; McGraw-Hill Book Co.

How to Get Ahead in a Defense Plant, by K. C. Hawthorne, Thomas Y. Crowell Co.

How to Read Aircraft Blueprints, by A. A. Owens; Winston Publishing Co.

Instrument and Radio Flying, by K. S. Day; Air Associates, Inc.

International Aviation Yearbook; Pitman Publishing Corp.

Introduction to Aircraft Design, by Thomas P. Faulconer; McGraw-Hill Book Co.

Jane's All the World's Aircraft; Macmillan Co.

Jordanoff's Illustrated Aviation Dictionary, by Assen Jordanoff; Harper and Brothers.

Magnaflux Inspection Methods, by Doane and Thomas; Photopress, Inc.

Man Behind the Flight, The, by Assen Jordanoff; Harper and Brothers.

Mathematics for the Aviation Trades, by James Naidich; McGraw-Hill Book Co.

Metal Airplane Structures, by F. E. Loudy; Norman W. Henley Co.

Metals Handbook, by American Society for Metals, 7016 Euclid Ave., Cleveland, Ohio.

Parachutes for Airmen, by Charles Dixon; Pitman Publishing Corp.

Practical Aircraft Sheet-Metal Work, by R. H. Frazer and Orrin Bertheaume; McGraw-Hill Book Co.

Practical Mathematics of Aviation, by A. E. Downer; Pitman Publishing Corp.

Prevention of the Failure of Metals under Repeated Stress, Battelle Institute publication for U. S. Navy Bureau of Aeronautics; John Wiley & Sons.

Process Practices in the Aircraft Industry, by Frank D. Klein, Jr.; McGraw-Hill Book Co.

Simple Aerodynamics and the Airplane, War Department publication by C. N. Monteith; Ronald Press.

Simplified Definitions and Nomenclature for Aeronautics, by Leslie Thorpe; Aviation Press.

Standard Aircraft Worker's Manual, Fletcher Aircraft Schools publication, Burbank, Calif.

Story of Aircraft, The, by Chelsea Fraser; Thomas Y. Crowell Co.

Structural Design of Metal Airplanes, by John Younger; McGraw-Hill Book Co.

Technical Aerodynamics, by K. D. Wood; McGraw-Hill Book Co.

Textbook on Aviation, A, by L. A. Thorp; Aviation Press.

Theory of Flight and Aircraft Engines, by Bert A. Shields; McGraw-Hill Book Co.

Through the Overcast; The Art of Instrument Flying, by Assen Jordanoff; Funk & Wagnalls Co.

Treatise on Aviation Law, by H. G. Hotchkiss; Baker, Voorhis & Co.

Types of Aircraft and Materials, by F. W. Wead; International Textbook Co.

Welding Handbook; American Welding Society.

American Aeronautical Periodicals

Aero Digest, 515 Madison Ave., New York, N. Y.

Aero Equipment Review, 1401 Third Ave., South, Minneapolis, Minn.

Air Facts, 30 Rockefeller Plaza, New York, N. Y.

Airlanes, 410 North Michigan Ave., Chicago, Ill.

Air Line Pilot, 3145 West 63rd St., Chicago, Ill.

Air Tech, 545 Fifth Ave., New York, N. Y.

Air Trails, 79 Seventh Ave., New York, N. Y.

American Aviation, Earle Bldg., Washington, D. C.

Aviation, 330 West 42nd St., New York, N. Y.

Journal of the Aeronautical Sciences, 30 Rockefeller Plaza, New York, N. Y.

Journal of Air Law, 357 East Chicago Ave., Chicago, Ill.

Journal of Aviation Medicine, 2642 University Ave., St. Paul, Minn.

National Aeronautics, Dupont Circle, Washington, D. C.

Notice to Aviators, Hydrographic Office, Washington, D. C.

Official Aviation Guide, 608 South Dearborn St., Chicago, Ill.

Pilot, The, Grand Central Air Terminal, Glendale, Calif.
Popular Aviation, 608 South Dearborn St., Chicago, Ill.
U. S. Air Services, Transportation Bldg., Washington, D. C.
Weekly Air Commerce Bulletin, Washington, D. C.

INDEX

A

AC specifications, 79
Acetate dopes, 71
Acetylene flame, 140, 193
Administration, 1-2
Aerodynamics, 9 ff.
Aging alloys, 42, 159
Ailerons, 20-21, 193-194
Air brakes, 21, 194
Aircraft classifications, CAA, 14
Aircraft finish code, 175-176
Aircraft plumbing, 113
Aircraft types and nomenclature, 13 ff.
Airfoil, 9, 19, 194
  section, choosing, 29
Air forces, 10-11, 31
Air Forces welding specifications, 145-146
Airscrew, 9-10, 194
Airworthiness regulations, CAA, 32, 194
Alclad, 47, 48, 195
  minimum Rockwell readings for, 153
Alloying elements, 61 ff.
Alloys:
  aluminum, 43, 44 ff.
  A.I.S.I. designations, 56
  carbon steel, 56
  defined, 195
  magnesium, 58-60
  steel, 51 ff.
  wrought, 46, 49
Aluminathus, 45
Aluminum, 38, 44 ff.
  corrosion resistance, 47
  extrusions, 51
  oxide coating, 48
  welding, 141, 143 ff.
  working with, 48-51
Aluminum alloys, 44 ff., 160, 162-163
  die castings, 50
  heat treating, 43, 158
  minimum Rockwell readings for, 153
  strength and specification numbers for, 162-163
  surface protection for, 47
  symbolic sectioning, 78
  welding, 144-146
  working with, 48-51
Aluminum Company of America, 143
American Iron & Steel Institute alloys, 56
American Magnesium symbols, 59
American National Standard thread, 87-88
American Standards Assn. line alphabet, 74, 75
Amphibians, 16, 27
Angle plate, 125
Angle template, 36
Annealing, 42, 43-44, 196
Anodic test, 156
Anodizing, 5, 47-48, 156, 196
AN specifications, 79
Anti-sieze paste, 117
Anvils, for hardness test, 152
Aquaplane, 11
Arc welding, 135 ff.
Army aircraft designations, 13
Army Air Force specifications, welding, 145-146
Army-Navy specifications, 79
  Parts Book, 82, 83-87
Army-Navy standard for nuts, bolts, etc., 53
Army specifications, 79

Assembly, 5 ff., 123 ff.
Assembly boards, 33
Atomic hydrogen welding, 135, 146-
147
Austentic stainless steel, 63
Auxiliary airfoils, 19
Auxiliary power unit, 17, 196

B

Babbitt metal:
defined, 197
symbolic sectioning, 78
Baby Brinell tester, 154
Backward welding, 142
Baekeland, Dr., 67
Bakelite, 67
Balance schedule, 30
Ball penetrator, 153
Barrel plating, 65-66
Bar steels, 54
Base line, 35
Bauxite, 44-45
Bending allowances, 107-113, 171
Beryllium, 38, 60-61
Biplane, 16, 21-22
Blade Element Theory, 10
Blisters, 69
Blocks, 125-126
Block template, 36
Blueprints, 3, 33, 73, 173-175
Body plan, 35
Bolts, 87-89
Bourdon tube, 198
Brale penetrator, 153
Brass:
composition and uses, 62
symbolic sectioning, 78
Brighteners, 67
Brinell hardness testing, 154
Brittleness of metals, 39
Bronze:
composition and uses, 62
defined, 198
symbolic sectioning, 78
Brown & Sharp gage, 49
B-17 Flying Fortress bomber, 13

B-24 Liberator bomber, 12
Bucking bar, 128
Built-up jig, 124
Bumping forms, 35
Bunsen, Robert, 44
Buttock line, 35
Button-head screw, 89
Butt-resistance welding, 137-138

C

Cadmium plating, 5, 57, 64-67
Calipers, 102
Carbon, 61
Carbonizing flame, 140
Carbon steel, 52
alloys, 55-56
Carburizing, 42, 54
Carrier plane, 16
Case-hardening, 42, 54, 199
Castings, 50
Cast iron, symbolic sectioning, 78
Castle nut, 90
Castle shear nut, 90
Cast steel, 53
Cast type jig, 124, 125
Cellulose acetates, 68
Check nut, 90
Chemical elements and symbols, 182-
183
Chemical laboratories, 4
Chrome-molybdenum steel, 53, 54
Chrome-pickle treatment, magnesium,
60
Chrome-vanadium steel, 53, 54
Chromium, 63
Chromium steels, 52
Chromodizing, 48
Circular magnetization, 151
Civil Aeronautics Authority:
aircraft classifications, 14
airworthiness regulations, 32
Clamp and packing block, 125
Clevis bolt, 88, 89
Cobalt, 63
Cockpit, 23

Color chart for raw materials, 166-168
Color marking, carbon steel alloys, 55-56
Columbium, 54, 63
Conductivity, electrical, 40, 200
Construction characteristics, aircraft, 14-17
Contour template, 36
Contraction and expansion of metals, 40
Contracts, 1, 2
Control diagram, 19-20
Control pulleys, 92-93
Copper, 62
Copper-beryllium alloy, 61
Corrosion:
defined, 200
magnesium alloys, 60
steels, 57-58
Corrosion resistance:
aluminum, 47
steel, 53
Cost estimates, 2
Cotter pins, 93-94
Counterpressing, 133-135
Countersunk riveting, 133, 134
Cowl flaps, 19, 201
Customer representatives, 2

D

Davis wing, 12
Deep V anvil, 152
Degreaser, 57
Density of metals, 40
Deoxidizing, 61
Depth gage, 104
micrometer, 107
Design, detailed, 32-33
Design principles, 28 ff.
Diagonal proof line, 35
Die castings, 50
Dill Manufacturing Co., 96
Dimensional inspections, 155
Dimensions, drafting rules for, 77
Dimpling set, use of, 134

Dividers, 101-102
Dope or paint dept., 5
Dopes, 69
and fabrics, 38, 70-71
Dow Chemical Co., 59
treatment No. 7, 60
Drafting, 74
department, 32
rules, 77
Drag forces, 10-11, 202
Drawings, 74 ff.
Drilled hex-head bolt, 89
Drilling, 129
Drill-jig template, 36
Drill press, 129
Drill sizes, 181
Drill template, 36
Drzewieski, 10
Ductility of metals, 39
Dural rivets, 126
Duralumin, 202
Dzus fasteners, 94-96

E

Eggshell fuselage, 23
Elasticity of metals, 39-40
Elastic limit, 41
Electrical conductivity, 40
Electrical dept., 5
Electric arc welders, 146-147
Electricians, 7
Electric welding, 135
Electric winding, symbolic sectioning, 78
Electrode size for metallic-arc welds, 145
Elevators, 20, 26, 203
Empirical formula, 108, 203
Engine, 17, 203-204
and propeller forces, 32
build-up and assembly dept., 5
installation, 5
selection, 28-29
Engineering sections, 3
Expansion of metals, 40
Experimental and planning dept., 2

Explosive rivets, 98-99
Extrusions, 49-50, 51

F

Fabrics and dopes, 70-71
Factory operation, 1 ff.
Fasteners:
  Dzus, 94-96
  Lok-Skru, 96-98
  type D, 97-98
Feeler set thickness gage, 102-104
Felt insulation, symbolic sectioning, 78
Ferritic stainless steel, 63
Files, 120-122
Fillister-head screw, 89
Final assembly, 7, 123
Final finish, 7
Final test and inspection, 7
Firewall, 19, 205
Fittings, 113, 205
  metal for, 53
  types of, 115
Fixed pitch propeller, 17
Fixtures, 123, 124-126
  department, 5
Flames, welding, 140
Flaring, 113-116
Flash welding, 137-138
Flat-head screw, 89
Flat patterns, 33
Flat template, 36
Flight test dept., 8
Floats, 27, 205
Flush riveting, 133-134
Flux, 141
Flying boat, 16, 27, 24-25
Flying Fortresses, 13
Foot pedals, 21
Ford Willow Run plant, 135
Form blocks, 33
Formulas and processes, new, 4
Forward welding, 142
Fuel lines, self-sealing, 71-72
Full cantilever wing, 22
Functions of numbers, 188-191

Fuselage:
  defined, 206
  department, 5
  nomenclature, 23
  rings, 23
  stationing, 18
Fusibility, 40

G

Gages, 102-104, 105, 177
Gage template, 36
Gas welding, 135, 139, 141
  torch tips for, 143
Glass, symbolic sectioning, 78
Go gage, 104-105
Goodrich Riv-Nuts, 99-101
Government contracts, 2
Ground reactions, 31-32
Grumman biplane nomenclature, 21-22
Gun riveting, 132-133

H

Hall, Charles Martin, 44
Hand motor, 129
Hardness of metals, 39
Hardness testing, 151-154, 178-179
Hard wire, 55
Heat treatment, 5, 39, 42-43, 158, 161
  test for, 153
Heliarc welding, 135, 136
Hermaphrodite calipers, 102
Heroult, Paul, 44
Hexagon Lok-Skru fastener, 97
Hex-head bolts, 89
Hex nuts, 90
Hull dept., 5
Hydraulics, 5, 7
  section, 5
Hydrodynamic forces, 11
Hydrogen welding, 141

I

Ice-box rivet, 126
Inconel, 54-55

Inertia and weight, 31
Inspection, 7-8, 148 ff.
  types of, 149-150
Inspection fluid, 151
Inspectors, requirements for, 148-149
Instruments, measuring, 101-107
Iron, and steel compared, 53
Isometric projection, 75-76

J

Jack (screw) and block, 126
J chart, 110
Jenny calipers, 102
Jigs, 123, 124-126, 207
Jigs, tools, and fixtures dept., 5
Joggling, 122, 172
Joystick, 21

K

Kilogram load, 152
Kinetic energy, 208

L

Lacquer, 71
Landing gear:
  defined, 208
  nomenclature, 26-27
Landplane, 16
Layouts, 35
  nomenclature, 35 ff.
Lead, 63
  symbolic sectioning, 78
Liberator bomber, 12
Lift, 9, 10-11, 208
Light-gage aluminum, welding, 144
Line alphabet, 74, 75
Line welding, 138
Lock washers, 91
Loft floor, 34, 35
Lofting, 33-37
  nomenclature, 35 ff.
Lok-Skru fastener, 96-98
Longitudinal magnetization, 151

M

Machine screw hex nut, 90
Machine settings, aluminum welding, 145
Magnaflux inspection, 151
Magnesium, 38
  alloys, 58-60
  rivets, 59
  symbolic sectioning, 78
Magnetic inspection method, 150-151
Mahogany plywood, 70
Maintenance of plant, 3-4
Malleability of metals, 39
Manganese, 61
  steels, 52
Marking template, 36
Martensitic stainless steel, 63
Master layouts, 35
Master router template, 36
Materials and processes, 38 ff.
Measuring instruments, 101-107
Mechanical inspection, 149
Melting point of metals, 40
Metalizing, 64
Metallic-arc welds, 145
Metallurgical tests, 41 ff.
Metallurgy, 39-42
Metals, physical properties, 39-40
Micrometers, 105-107
Mock-up, 30-31
Models, 2, 30
Moh's scale, 151
Mold line, 35
Molybdenum, 54, 63
  steels, 52
Monocoque fuselage, 23
Monoplane, 16
  wing, 22
Move jig, 124
Multiplane, 16

N

Nacelles, 19, 209
NAF specifications, 79

National Advisory Committee for Aeronautics, 16
Navy designations, 13-14
Navy specifications, 79
Navy welding specifications, 147
Neoprene, 71-72, 209
Neutral flame, 140
Nibbler template, 36
Nickel, 62-63, 209
-chromium steels, 52
steels, 52
Nitrogen, 63
Nomenclature:
aircraft, 13 ff.
layout, 35 ff.
loft, 35 ff.
power-plant, 17-19
template, 35 ff.
Normalizing process, 42, 57
Northrup aircraft factory, 135
Northrup wing, 12
Not Go gage, 104-105
Nuts, 88-91
metal for, 53
Nut plates, 90
Nylon, 209

O

Oblique projection, 75-76
Officers, company, 1
Oleo struts, 26-27, 210
One-shot riveting gun, 132-133
Organizational setup, 1
Orthographic projection, 76-77
Oxide, 139
Oxidizing flame, 140
Oxy-acetylene gas welders, 146-147
Oxy-hydrogen welders, 146-147

P

Packing block, 125
Paint dept., 5
Painting aluminum alloys, 48
Paint tests, 155

Parallel blocks, 125
Parts and processes section, 4-5
Parts dept., 4
Passivating, 57
Penetrators, 152, 153
Phenolic resins, 68
Phillips screw head, 119
Phosphorus, 61
Pickling:
aluminum alloys, 51
steel, 57, 58
Pictorial drawing, 75, 77
Pilot's compartment, 23
Pitch, propeller, 17-18, 210-211
Plane anvil, 152
Plane of symmetry, 10
Planning dept., 2
Plant maintenance, 3-4
Plastics, 38, 67-70
Plexiglass, 69
Plug gages, 104
Plug screws, Riv-Nut, 101
Plywood, 70, 211
Policies, company, 1
Polymerization, 68
Portable squeezer, 131
Power-plant:
housing, 19
nomenclature, 17-19
Primary assembly, 5-7, 123
Processes:
and materials, 38 ff.
new, 4
Production breakdown, light bomber, 6
Production engineering dept., 3
Profile template, 37
Project coordinators, 3
Projections, oblique and isometric, 75-76
Proof stress, 41
Propeller, 9-10, 17, 211-212
and engine forces, 32
Prototype, 33
Pulleys, control, 92-93
Purchasing dept., 4
Pusher airplane, 16

Q

Quadruplane, 16
Qualification tests for welders, 146-147
Quaternary magnesium alloys, 58

R

Radio and electrical dept., 5
Receiving dept., 4
Reed & Prince screw head, 119
Rejection, causes for, 132, 149-150
Reprecipitation, 42
Resistance welding, 137-138
Retractable gear, 26-27
Ring gages, 104
Riveters, 5
Riveting, 123-124, 126 ff.
Rivets:
  characteristics, 127
  dural, 126
  explosive, 98-99
  magnesium, 59
  measurement, 128
  rejection, causes for, 132
  spacing chart, 129-130
  standard sizes, 169
Riv-Nuts, Goodrich, 99-101
Rockwell hardness testing, 151-153, 154
Round-head screw, 89
Router template, 37
Rubber:
  symbolic sectioning, 78
  synthetic, 71-72
Rudder, 19, 20, 26, 213
  bar, 21, 213
Rule, 101
Ryan Aeronautical Co., 135

S

Safety factor, 32
Salt-spray test, 155
Salvage, 8
Sand blasting, 57, 213

Sand casting, alloy, 50
Scales, 101
Screwdrivers, 118
Screw heads, special, 118-119
Screw jack, 126
Screw thread gage, 103
Screws, 87-89
Scribers, 101-102
Scrieve-board layout, 36
Seamless tubing, 113
Seam welding, 138
  machine settings for aluminum alloys, 145
Seaplane, 16, 27
Selenium sulphides, 54
Self-locking hex nut, 90
Semicantilever wing, 22
Semimonocoque fuselage, 23
Service dept., 8
Set-back, 110-111, 112
Shafts, metal for, 53
Shallow V anvil, 152
Sheet metals, 49
Shellac, 67
Ship-plane, 16
Shop practice, 73 ff., 149-150
⅛ Shrink template, 37
Side forces, 10-11
Silicon, 61-62
Silicon-manganese steels, 53
Sketches, 73
Slag, 139
Slow butt welding, 137-138
Slow hitter riveting gun, 132-133
Soap-and-water tests, 155
Society of Automotive Engineers, 51
Socket wrenches, 118
Special specifications, 79-80
Specifications, 28, 79-87
Specific gravity, 40
Spinning machine, 113
Specifications, listing of, 80-82
Spot anvil, 152
Spot-welding, 137, 138
Spraying, metal, 64
Spring back, aluminum alloys, 49

Springs, beryllium-aluminum alloys, 60-61
Squeeze riveting, 131-132
Stabilizers, 23, 26, 215
Stainless steel, 53-54, 55, 63
  marking, 56
  pickling, 58
Standard landing gear, 26
Stationary landing gear, 26
Stationing, 17, 18
Steel, 38, 51 ff., 158, 161, 164-165
  and iron, 53
  annealing, 44, 57
  colors, 158
  heat treating, 161
  kinds, 51-53
  marking system, 55
  producing processes, 53
  special processes, 56-58
  stainless (*see* Stainless steel)
  strength and specification numbers for, 164-165
  symbolic sectioning, 78
  wire, 55
Still plating, 65-66
Stock clerks, 4
Stock template, 37
Strain, 41
Stranded wire, 55
Stress, 41, 216
  analysis, 31-32
Stress-and-strain tests, 41, 155
Stretcher-leveling, 49
Stripe code, 55-56
Stripping test, 154
Sulphur, 61
Superficial Rockwell tester, 154
Surface controls, 19-21, 217
Symbols, magnesium alloys, 59
Synthetic rubber, 71-72

T

Tail:
  assembly dept., 5
  construction characteristics, 15
  sections, 23, 26

Tailless airplane, 12
Tandem airplane, 16
Taper pin, 94
  washer, 91
Taps, 119
Temperature conversion, 170
Templates, 33, 217-218
  nomenclature, 35 ff.
Tensile strength, 41
  steels, 51, 55
Ternary magnesium alloys, 58
Testing laboratories, 4
Test pilot, 8
Tests:
  hardness, 151-153
  paint, 155
  stress and strain, 155
  wind tunnel, 30
Termoplastic materials, 69
Thermosetting plastic materials, 68-69
Thickness gages, 102-104
Thiokol, 71-72, 218
Thread die, 119-120
Threads, 87-88
  gages, 103, 104, 106, 193
Thrust airfoils, 9
Tie-rods, 55
Titanium, 54, 63
Tolerances, 33, 218
Toolmaker, 5
Tools:
  department, 5
  designing, 3
Torch tips for gas welding, 143
Torch welding:
  heliarc, 136
  torch, 141
Torque moment, 117, 218
Torque wrenches, 116-117
Toughness of metals, 40
Tractor airplane, 16
Trichlorethlene vapor, 57
Tricycle landing gear, 26
Trimming tabs, 21, 217
Trim template, 37
Triplane, 16
Tube bending, 114

Tube flaring, 113-116
Tubing, 113
Tumble home, 35
Tune-up mechanic, 7
Tungsten, 63, 219
Turnbuckle assemblies, 91-92
Type D fastener, 97-98

U

Ultimate-load factor, 32
Urea plastics, 68

V

Vanadium, 63, 219
V blocks, 125
Vertical welding, 142
Vibrator riveting gun, 132-133
Vinyls, 68
Visual inspection, 149
Vixen files, 121

W

Washers, 88-91
Water, symbolic sectioning, 78
Waterline, 35
Water tests, 155
Weight and inertia forces, 31
Weights and specific gravities, 157
Welded jigs, 124
Welders, 7
  tests for, 146-147
Welding, 123-124, 135-141, 220-221
  aluminum, 142 ff.
  department, 5
  flames, 140
  torch, 136, 141

"Welding Procedure for Certification of
  Welders," 145-147
Willow Run plant, 135
Windshields, 69
Wind-tunnel tests, 30, 221
Wing:
  construction characteristics, 14-15
  Davis, 12
  defined, 221
  department, 5
  design, 29
  flaps, 21
  function of, 9
  nomenclature, 21 ff.
  Northrup, 12
  stationing, 18
  types, 21-22
Wire drawing, 221
Wire, steel, 55
Wire tightener, 91
Wood, symbolic sectioning, 78
Wooden jigs, 125
Work-hardening, 39
Workmanship standards, 150
Wrenches:
  socket, 118
  torque, 116-117
Wrought alloys, 46, 49
Wrought steel, 53

Y

Yield factor, 32, 40
Yield point, 41
Yield strength, 41

Z

Zero welding, 135
Zirconium sulphides, 54

The Aviation Collection by Sportsman's Vintage Press

www.SportsmansVintagePress.com

Aircraft Construction Handbook	by Thomas A. Dickinson
Aircraft Sheet Metal Work	by C. A. LeMaster
The Aircraft Apprentice	by Leslie MacGregor
Aircraft Woodwork	by Col. R. H. Drake
Aircraft Welding	by Col. R. H. Drake
Aircraft Sheet Metal	by Col. R. H. Drake
Aircraft Engines	by Col. R. H. Drake
Aircraft Electrical and Hydraulic Systems, and Aircraft Instruments	by Col. R. H. Drake
Aircraft Engine Maintenance and Service	by Col. R. H. Drake
Aircraft Maintenance and Service	by Col. R. H. Drake

Made in the USA
Las Vegas, NV
26 March 2022